No Gallbladder Diet Cookbook

Rebalance and Revitalize Your Body with Delicious and Nutritious Recipes After Gallbladder Removal. Includes a 45-Day Meal Plan

Arielle Hawthorne

TABLE OF CONTENTS

Chapter 1: Understanding the Gallbladder and Its Removal

The Role of the Gallbladder in Digestion

The gallbladder, a small organ tucked beneath the liver, might seem inconspicuous, but its role in our digestive orchestra is significant. Primarily, the gallbladder serves as a reservoir for bile, a yellowish-green fluid produced by the liver. This bile is not just a random fluid; it's a crucial digestive agent, particularly in the breakdown of fats. When we consume fat-rich foods, the gallbladder springs into action, releasing bile into the small intestine. Here's where the magic happens: bile emulsifies fats, essentially breaking them down into smaller droplets. This process is vital because it makes fats more accessible to lipase, an enzyme that further digests these fats into fatty acids and glycerol.

But why is this process so important? Consider fats as complex, hard-to-digest nutrients. Without proper breakdown, these fats can pass through our digestive system, largely unabsorbed, leading to nutritional deficiencies and digestive discomfort. Moreover, the breakdown of fats facilitates the absorption of fat-soluble vitamins (A, D, E, and K), which play pivotal roles in everything from vision to blood clotting, bone health to immune function.

The gallbladder's role doesn't end here. Bile also aids in the elimination of waste products from the body. Certain substances, including cholesterol and bilirubin (a byproduct of red blood cell breakdown), are excreted from the body in bile. Without this excretion mechanism, these substances could accumulate to harmful levels.

In understanding the gallbladder's role, it's important to note that it's not the bile producer but the bile storer. The liver continuously produces bile, but in the absence of dietary fats, this bile has no immediate role. Here, the gallbladder steps in, storing and concentrating this bile until it's needed. This storage capability is what makes the gallbladder unique; it ensures a ready supply of concentrated bile at the exact moment it's needed for efficient fat digestion.

Understanding the gallbladder's function is crucial, especially considering the dietary implications of its removal. When the gallbladder is removed, the body loses its primary bile storage facility. This doesn't stop bile production, but it changes the way bile is delivered to the intestines. Instead of a concentrated burst of bile released in response to fats, the liver drips bile continuously into the small intestine. This change can impact the efficiency of fat digestion and the body's ability to absorb those crucial fat-soluble vitamins.

Moreover, without the gallbladder's concentrated bile, the process of emulsifying fats becomes less efficient. This can lead to changes in digestion and dietary needs, particularly in the way fats are consumed and processed. Post-gallbladder removal, it's often recommended to adjust fat intake, focusing on smaller, more frequent meals with moderate fat content to align with the continuous, less concentrated flow of bile.

The gallbladder's absence also underscores the importance of a diet that supports liver health and ensures optimal bile production. Nutrients that promote liver health become paramount, as the liver now bears the sole responsibility for managing bile and its role in digestion.

In summary, the gallbladder, though small, plays a mighty role in digestion, particularly in fat processing and waste elimination. Understanding its function is the first step in navigating the dietary adjustments necessary after its removal. As we delve deeper into the nuances of a gallbladder-less digestive system, the focus shifts to adapting our diet and lifestyle to maintain nutritional balance and digestive comfort, a journey that requires both knowledge and mindful adjustments.

Reasons for Gallbladder Removal

Embarking on a journey without your gallbladder may seem daunting at first. The decision to remove this pear-shaped organ, nestled beneath your liver, is never taken lightly. Often, it's the culmination of a complex interplay of health factors, each resonating with the unique narratives of those who walk this path.

At the heart of many gallbladder removal stories are gallstones, crystalline formations that emerge like unwelcome guests in the gallbladder. These stones range from the size of a grain of sand to that of a golf ball, and their presence can disrupt the serene flow of digestion. Imagine these stones as tiny intruders, causing blockages and triggering pain, often intense enough to eclipse the rhythms of daily life.

In other scenarios, the gallbladder itself rebels, becoming inflamed or infected - a condition known as cholecystitis. This inflammation can be acute, arising suddenly like a storm, or chronic, a relentless, simmering discomfort.

Sometimes, the gallbladder becomes a stage for more serious concerns, like gallbladder cancer. Though rare, such instances necessitate removal for the broader sake of health.

Let's also not forget the silent yet impactful condition of biliary dyskinesia. Here, the gallbladder, though devoid of stones, fails in its rhythmic dance of contraction and release, leading to chronic pain and digestive woes.

Each of these conditions, while distinct in their manifestations, share a common resolution: cholecystectomy, or the surgical removal of the gallbladder. This procedure, though common, marks the beginning of a new chapter in one's dietary narrative.

The decision for removal often follows a trail of consultations, reflections, and evaluations. It's not merely a clinical conclusion but a deeply personal one, influenced by the nuances of individual health landscapes and life stories.

For many, this decision is a pivot towards relief, a step away from the relentless pain and discomfort that shadowed their days. It's a move towards normalcy, towards embracing daily activities without the lurking fear of a gallstone attack or the unpredictable pangs of cholecystitis.

In essence, gallbladder removal is often less about the loss of an organ and more about regaining a quality of life. It's about soothing the body's cries of distress and paving a path for smoother digestion and a more harmonious existence.

As you turn the page on your gallbladder, it's crucial to remember that this is not an end, but a beginning. A beginning of understanding your body's new rhythms, of embracing dietary adaptations, and of nurturing your health with renewed vigilance and care.

In the coming chapters, we will explore the intricacies of these adaptations, guiding you through a dietary landscape reshaped by the absence of your gallbladder. We'll uncover the secrets of managing your digestion, of choosing foods that harmonize with your body's new needs, and of living a full, vibrant life post-surgery.

Your journey without a gallbladder is not just about adjusting to a new way of eating; it's about rekindling a relationship with your body, listening to its signals, and nourishing it with kindness and understanding. It's a journey of rediscovery, resilience, and rejuvenation.

Life After Gallbladder Surgery: What Changes?

Embarking on life post-gallbladder removal, known as cholecystectomy, opens a new chapter in the book of your body's narrative. This section delves into the post-surgical journey, highlighting the changes and adaptations that unfold in your digestive story.

Once the gallbladder, that small but mighty organ, parts ways with your body, the dynamics of digestion undergo a transformation. The gallbladder's role – storing and concentrating bile produced by the liver – ceases, and thus, the way bile enters your digestive tract changes fundamentally. Instead of being released in controlled bursts, bile now drips continuously into the intestines. This shift, seemingly minor, has ripple effects throughout the digestive process.

The most immediate change is the body's altered response to fatty foods. Without the gallbladder's concentrated bile to break down large fat globules, the digestive system may initially fumble with high-fat meals. This can lead to experiences that range from mildly uncomfortable to acutely distressing – bloating, gas, and changes in bowel habits are common initial companions in this journey.

Yet, the human body is a marvel of adaptation. Over time, the liver ups its game, adjusting bile production to this new normal. Gradually, the digestive system recalibrates, learning to process fats more efficiently even in the absence of the gallbladder. This adaptation period varies, painting a unique recovery canvas for each individual.

For many, this transition period is peppered with trial and error. It's a time of learning which foods play well with their new digestive landscape and which ones stir up the waters. Low-fat diets often become a temporary harbor in this stormy phase, offering respite as the body navigates through these uncharted waters.

Yet, it's not just about subtracting fats. It's about redefining the relationship with food. It's about discovering that balance where nourishment and enjoyment coexist. Foods rich in fiber – fruits, vegetables, whole grains – step into the spotlight, aiding digestion and adding color to the dietary palette.

The changes, however, transcend the physical. This journey is as much about the body as it is about the mind. It's about cultivating patience and kindness towards oneself, understanding that the body's pace of healing and adaptation is a deeply personal affair. It's about learning to listen to the subtle whispers of the body, discerning what feels good and what doesn't.

Amidst these changes, some find their culinary creativity ignited. Experimenting with new recipes, exploring the world of herbs and spices, and embracing a variety of plant-based foods become pathways to joy and healing. The kitchen transforms into a lab of delicious experiments, each meal a step towards understanding and harmonizing with this new bodily rhythm.

For others, the journey is less about experimentation and more about finding comfort in simplicity. It's about crafting meals that are gentle, nourishing, and reassuring – foods that soothe rather than challenge the digestive system.

Navigating this post-cholecystectomy landscape is not a solitary journey. Support systems – be they healthcare professionals, fellow gallbladder-less voyagers, or supportive family and friends – play a pivotal role. They are the compasses and lighthouses, guiding through rough seas and illuminating paths of wellness and comfort.

As the narrative of life without a gallbladder unfolds, one theme resonates: resilience. The body's ability to adapt, the spirit's capacity to embrace change, and the heart's openness to rewrite its dietary story are testaments to human resilience. This journey, though dotted with challenges, is also strewn with opportunities – to rediscover food, to listen to one's body, and to nourish oneself in more holistic, mindful ways.

In the chapters to follow, we'll delve deeper into this narrative. We'll explore the specific dietary adaptations, the practical tips, and the wholesome recipes that align with your new digestive reality. We'll journey together through the landscapes of post-gallbladder nutrition, discovering ways to thrive, indulge, and celebrate food in its myriad forms.

As you step forward into this new chapter, remember: change, though daunting, is also a doorway to discovery. And in this discovery lies the potential for a richer, more attuned, and vibrant dietary life.

Chapter 2: The Impact on Your Diet and Digestion

How Digestion Changes Without a Gallbladder

In the grand tapestry of the human body, each organ plays a pivotal role, harmonizing in an intricate ballet of function and form. The gallbladder, often unassuming in its presence, becomes notably significant by its absence. Its departure ushers in a new era in the realm of digestion, an era marked by adaptation and resilience.

When the gallbladder is removed, the body's method of handling fats undergoes a significant transformation. The gallbladder's primary role – to store bile produced by the liver and release it during the digestion of fats – is now a chapter of the past. In its absence, the liver assumes the role of the sole provider of bile, but with a twist. Instead of releasing bile in concentrated bursts, the liver now trickles it continuously into the small intestine.

This change, subtle yet profound, alters the digestive landscape. Bile, a detergent-like fluid, is essential for emulsifying fats, breaking them down into smaller droplets. This process is crucial as it prepares fats for further digestion and absorption by enzymes in the intestine. In the gallbladder-less body, the absence of regulated bile release can lead to challenges in digesting large amounts of fat at once. This shift often manifests in a spectrum of digestive responses ranging from mild discomfort to more pronounced symptoms like bloating, gas, and changes in bowel habits.

Yet, the body is not a static entity but a dynamic ecosystem capable of remarkable adjustments. Over time, the liver adapts to this new role, modulating bile production to meet the continuous demand. The digestive system, a marvel of flexibility and adaptation, gradually learns to process fats more efficiently, even in the absence of gallbladder's targeted bile release.

In this new digestive chapter, the diet naturally gravitates towards a central role. It becomes a powerful tool, a means of harmonizing with the body's altered fat digestion capabilities. This is not a narrative of restriction but one of balance and mindfulness. It involves understanding the types of fats and their impact on a gallbladder-less digestion.

Saturated and trans fats, often found in processed and fried foods, pose a more significant challenge to digest and may exacerbate discomfort. On the other hand, monounsaturated and polyunsaturated fats, found in foods like avocados, nuts, and fish, are generally easier to manage and offer a healthier alternative.

Portion control also emerges as a key player in this new dietary game. Smaller, more frequent meals can ease the digestive process, preventing the overload of fat that can occur with larger, less frequent eating episodes. This approach allows for a gentler, more manageable digestion, aligning with the body's revised bile production rhythm.

Fiber, a vital component of the diet, assumes an enhanced role. Soluble fiber, in particular, found in foods like oats, apples, and carrots, can aid in the absorption of bile acids in the intestine, promoting a smoother digestive process. This is especially beneficial in preventing the diarrhea that some individuals experience post-gallbladder removal.

The narrative of digestion without a gallbladder is also one of individual experiences and responses. Each body scripts its own adaptation story, with some adjusting swiftly while others navigate a longer road to dietary harmony. It's a journey marked by patience, observation, and adjustment. It involves tuning into the body's signals, understanding its new language, and responding with dietary choices that resonate with its needs.

The absence of the gallbladder also invites a deeper engagement with food. It's an opportunity to explore new recipes, to experiment with diverse ingredients, and to embrace a style of eating that is both nourishing and fulfilling. It's about crafting meals that are gentle on the digestive system yet rich in flavor and nutrients.

This chapter of digestion without a gallbladder is not just about the mechanics of food breakdown. It's about building a relationship with food that is reflective, intentional, and attuned to the body's evolved needs. It's about finding joy and satisfaction in meals that not only taste good but also feel good.

As we progress through this chapter, the narrative will unfold further, revealing practical, actionable advice on navigating this new dietary landscape. We will explore the nuances of food choices, the art of meal planning, and the joy of discovering a diet that resonates with your body's new rhythm.

In essence, life after gallbladder removal is a journey of discovery – a discovery of how the body adapts, how diet can be tailored, and how every meal can be a step towards harmonious digestion and overall well-being.

Nutritional Considerations and Adjustments

After the gallbladder's departure from your bodily constellation, the way you nourish yourself enters a new era. This isn't merely a phase of adjustment; it's an evolution, a renaissance of dietary understanding. The absence of the gallbladder ushers in a need for mindful eating, where each choice at the dining table becomes a stitch in the fabric of your well-being.

The primary shift in nutritional focus, post-gallbladder removal, orbits around the metabolism of fats. The gallbladder's role in storing and releasing bile - crucial for fat digestion - is no longer in play. The liver, now the sole manager of bile, adjusts its production, but this bile is less concentrated and released continuously. The result? A digestive system that's more sensitive to high-fat feasts.

This doesn't spell an end to enjoying fats - a vital energy source and a necessity for absorbing fat-soluble vitamins (A, D, E, and K). Instead, it's about recalibrating the fat intake. It's about embracing healthy fats like those in avocados, olive oil, and nuts, while maintaining a watchful eye on the quantity. These facts are not just nutrient-dense but are also kinder to a gallbladder-less digestion.

Beyond fats, this new dietary chapter calls for a balanced macronutrient symphony - where proteins and carbohydrates play their parts harmoniously. Lean proteins, such as chicken, fish, and plant-based options, should be the cornerstone of your meals. They provide essential amino acids without burdening your digestion. Carbohydrates, especially complex ones like whole grains, legumes, and a bounty of fruits and vegetables, add fiber to this mix. Fiber, the unsung hero of digestion, takes on a greater role here, aiding in smoother digestive processes and offering a sense of satiety.

The art of portion control becomes an invaluable tool in your dietary arsenal. Smaller, more frequent meals can prevent the digestive system from being overwhelmed, especially when it comes to managing fat intake. This approach aligns beautifully with the continuous bile drip, allowing for better fat emulsification and absorption.

Hydration, often overlooked, is a crucial piece of the puzzle. Adequate water intake assists in digestion and helps maintain a healthy balance of nutrients in the body. It's the simplest, yet most profound act of nourishment you can offer yourself.

As you waltz through this dietary adaptation, it's essential to keep a food diary. This isn't just a log of what you eat; it's a narrative of your body's responses, a tale of what soothes and what irritates your digestive tract. This diary becomes a map, guiding your dietary choices, highlighting foods that are allies in your post-surgery journey.

Supplementation may step into the spotlight, especially if your body struggles to absorb certain nutrients post-removal. Vitamins A, D, E, and K, along with minerals like calcium and iron, might require a boost. However, this is a path to tread cautiously and always under the guidance of a healthcare professional.

Navigating social dining and holidays post-gallbladder removal is akin to learning a new dance. It's about finding balance, being selective without feeling deprived, and savoring flavors in moderation. It's about creating new traditions that honor your health and sharing these with others.

This chapter of your life is not just about subtracting or limiting. It's about expanding - your palate, your culinary skills, and your understanding of what it means to nourish yourself. It's about exploring new recipes, experimenting with herbs and spices, and discovering the joy in foods that love your back.

In essence, your post-gallbladder diet isn't a list of don'ts; it's a canvas of possibilities. It's a journey of learning to listen to your body, to honor its needs, and to find joy in the act of feeding it well. It's about building a relationship with food that's based on respect, understanding, and care.

Managing Digestive Symptoms Post-Surgery

Navigating the seas of your body's well-being post-gallbladder removal can feel like charting unknown waters. As the tides of your digestive system adjust to a new rhythm, it's crucial to become the captain of your dietary ship, steering through potential waves of discomfort with grace and knowledge.

Post-surgery, the body often signals its adjustment period through various digestive symptoms. These are not merely physical sensations but messages, clues to understanding and harmonizing with your body's new way of functioning. The most common companions in this journey are bloating, gas, diarrhea, and changes in bowel habits. While they may initially seem daunting, these symptoms are often manageable through thoughtful dietary choices and lifestyle adjustments.

Bloating and gas are often the body's protest against certain foods, especially those high in fats. This isn't just about the quantity of fats but their type. Foods laden with saturated and trans fats can be particularly troublesome. Reimagining your diet to include healthier fats in moderation, coupled with smaller, more frequent meals, can ease this discomfort. It's about finding a balance that allows your body to digest these foods without feeling overwhelmed.

Diarrhea, a common post-cholecystectomy symptom, can be a challenging wave to navigate. This often results from the continuous flow of bile into the intestines, which can irritate the gut lining. Incorporating soluble fiber, found in foods like oats, apples, and bananas, can be immensely helpful. Soluble fiber binds to bile acids, mitigating their irritating effect and adding bulk to stools. It's a gentle yet effective approach to calming the turbulent waters of post-surgical digestion.

Changes in bowel habits, whether it's more frequent bowel movements or a shift in consistency, are your body's way of adapting to its new digestive landscape. Keeping a food diary becomes an invaluable tool here, allowing you to track which foods harmonize with your system and which ones stir up the digestive waters. This isn't just a log; it's a dialogue with your body, a way of listening and responding to its needs.

Hydration plays a pivotal role in managing these symptoms. Drinking plenty of water not only aids in digestion but also helps in maintaining a healthy balance of nutrients and in the smooth functioning of the gut. Think of water as the soothing balm for your digestive tract, a simple yet profound gesture of care for your body.

Physical activity, too, can be a lighthouse guiding you through these symptoms. Gentle exercise, like walking or yoga, can stimulate digestion and aid in the movement of food through the digestive tract. It's not just about burning calories; it's about nurturing your body, giving it the movement, it craves to function optimally.

Sometimes, the journey may require a compass beyond what diet and lifestyle changes can provide. In such cases, seeking guidance from healthcare professionals for symptom management is not just advisable; it's essential. They can offer tailored advice, supplement strategies, or medication, if necessary, to ensure that your journey post-gallbladder removal is as smooth and comfortable as possible.

As you sail through this post-surgical phase, remember that these symptoms are often transient, markers of a body finding its new equilibrium. It's a journey of patience, understanding, and gentle adjustments. With each dietary and lifestyle adaptation, you're not just managing symptoms; you're crafting a deeper, more attuned relationship with your body.

Embrace this journey with an open heart and a curious mind. Experiment with foods, listen to your body's responses, and adjust your course as needed. This isn't a path of limitations but one of discovery and adjustment, leading you towards a life of comfort, balance, and well-being in your post-gallbladder world.

Chapter 3: Embracing a New Dietary Lifestyle

Mindset and Emotional Well-being

As you embark on this journey post-gallbladder removal, embracing a new dietary lifestyle is not just about the food you consume; it's about cultivating a mindset and emotional well-being that nourishes you from within. This holistic approach is the cornerstone of a sustainable and joyful transition to your new way of eating and living.

The process of adjusting to life without a gallbladder can be akin to learning a new language. It requires patience, practice, and a mindset open to exploration and adaptation. Embracing this change is not merely about adhering to a set of dietary rules; it's about rewriting your relationship with food and your body.

Begin by acknowledging the emotional landscape of this change. It's common to experience a spectrum of feelings – from relief after resolving painful symptoms to anxiety about adjusting to a new diet. Recognize that these emotions are natural companions on your journey, each offering insights into your relationship with your body and food.

Cultivating a positive mindset is pivotal. Instead of viewing the dietary changes as limitations, reframe them as opportunities for discovery and growth. Each meal becomes a canvas for creativity, each food choice an exploration of flavors and textures that align with your body's new needs.

Practice mindfulness in your eating habits. Mindful eating isn't just about what you eat; it's about how you eat. It involves being fully present during meals, savoring each bite, and listening to your body's hunger and fullness cues. This practice helps build a harmonious relationship with food, turning meals into a source of nourishment and pleasure rather than anxiety.

Emotional well-being is also nurtured through self-compassion. Be gentle with yourself as you navigate this change. Understand that there will be moments of trial and error, and that's okay. It's all part of the process of understanding what works best for your unique body.

Incorporate stress-reduction techniques into your routine. Stress can have a significant impact on digestion and overall well-being. Activities like yoga, meditation, or even simple breathing exercises can be effective in managing stress, contributing to a more balanced and healthy digestive system.

Remember, you're not alone on this journey. Building a supportive community – whether it's connecting with others who have undergone gallbladder removal, joined wellness groups, or simply shared your experiences with friends and family – can provide immense emotional support and encouragement. Sharing recipes, tips, and experiences can not only bolster your knowledge but also remind you that others share your path.

Educate yourself about your new dietary needs. Knowledge is empowering, and understanding the science behind your diet post-gallbladder removal can boost your confidence in making food choices. However, ensure that your sources are credible and that you're not swayed by dietary fads or misinformation.

Set realistic goals and celebrate your progress. Small victories, like trying a new recipe that agrees with your digestion or successfully managing a social dining situation, are milestones worth recognizing. They reinforce your capability to adapt and thrive in your new dietary lifestyle.

Embrace a holistic view of health. Your dietary changes are just one part of a larger picture of well-being. Engaging in regular physical activity, ensuring adequate sleep, and nurturing your mental health are equally important in maintaining a balanced and healthy life.

Finally, be patient with your journey. Adjusting to a new dietary lifestyle post-gallbladder removal is a gradual process, one that unfolds uniquely for each individual. Honor your body's pace, listen to its signals, and nourish it with kindness and understanding.

In this chapter, we're not just talking about changing what's on your plate; we're talking about transforming your approach to eating and living. It's a journey that goes beyond the kitchen, encompassing your mind, body, and spirit in a harmonious symphony of health and well-being.

Building a Supportive Culinary Environment

The journey to a new dietary lifestyle, particularly after gallbladder removal, is not just about the food you eat. It's also about creating a supportive culinary environment that nurtures your nutritional needs and aligns with your well-being goals. This environment extends beyond the kitchen, encompassing the psychological, social, and practical aspects of food in your life.

A supportive culinary environment begins in the heart of your home: the kitchen. This space should be your sanctuary, a place where healthy choices are easy to make and culinary exploration is encouraged. Start by reorganizing and restocking your kitchen. Clear out items that no longer align with your post-gallbladder dietary needs, and replace them with healthier alternatives. Stock up on spices, herbs, and condiments that add flavor without the fat. Ensure that you have the necessary tools for healthy cooking – a good set of knives, a blender for smoothies, and non-stick cookware for low-fat cooking.

Consider the arrangement of your kitchen. Place healthier food options in visible, easily accessible locations. For example, store fresh fruits on the countertop and place nutritious snacks at eye level in your pantry. This subtle method of organization can influence your food choices positively.

Create a meal planning routine. Having a plan can prevent last-minute, less-than-ideal food choices. Dedicate some time each week to meal planning. This doesn't mean every meal needs to be mapped out, but having a general idea of what you're going to eat can relieve the stress of decision-making and keep you on track with your dietary goals.

Incorporating variety into your meals is crucial. A diet that feels restrictive or monotonous can quickly become unsustainable. Experiment with different cuisines and recipes that comply with your post-surgery nutritional needs. This exploration not only makes your meals interesting but also helps you discover new dishes and ingredients that you enjoy.

A supportive culinary environment also means being mindful of how you eat. Create a pleasant dining atmosphere where you can eat slowly and savor your food. Eating in a relaxed setting can aid digestion and enhance the enjoyment of your meals.

Beyond the physical space, building a supportive culinary environment includes fostering positive social interactions around food. Share your dietary journey with friends and family. Educate them about your needs post-gallbladder removal so they can support you. Participating in cooking groups or online communities can also offer encouragement, share experiences, and exchange recipes.

Equip yourself with knowledge. Understanding the nutritional content of foods and how they affect your body post-surgery is empowering. This knowledge will enable you to make informed choices about what to eat and why. Read books, watch documentaries, or attend workshops to expand your understanding of nutrition and healthy cooking.

Be flexible and patient with yourself as you navigate this new culinary landscape. Dietary changes, especially following surgery, require an adjustment period. It's okay to have days when things don't go as planned. What's important is to stay committed to your overall goal of health and well-being.

Remember, building a supportive culinary environment is a dynamic process. As you grow and evolve in your dietary journey, so too will your needs and preferences. Be open to change and willing to adapt your environment accordingly.

In summary, creating a supportive culinary environment post-gallbladder removal is about more than just the foods you eat. It's about crafting a space and a lifestyle that encourages healthy eating, supports your nutritional needs, and makes your dietary journey enjoyable and sustainable. It's a holistic approach that considers not just the physical aspects of food but also the emotional and social dimensions, ensuring a balanced and fulfilling dietary lifestyle.

Tips for Grocery Shopping and Reading Labels

In the tapestry of your new dietary lifestyle post-gallbladder removal, the threads of grocery shopping and label reading are woven with particular importance. These tasks, though seemingly mundane, are in fact pivotal in ensuring your diet aligns harmoniously with your body's altered digestive capabilities.
Grocery Shopping: A Strategic Affair
Embarking on a grocery shopping expedition is no longer just a routine errand; it becomes a strategic affair, a mission to fill your cart with foods that not only tantalize your taste buds but also agree with your digestive system.
Plan Ahead: Before setting foot in the grocery store, arm yourself with a plan. Create a shopping list based on the meals you've planned for the week. This not only saves time but also helps you resist the siren call of impulse buys that may not align with your post-surgery dietary needs.
Perimeter Strategy: As a general rule, the healthiest foods in a grocery store are located along the perimeter. Here, you'll find fresh produce, lean proteins, and dairy alternatives. These should form the foundation of your diet.

Inner Aisles with Caution: Venture into the inner aisles with caution and purpose. This is where processed foods often lurk, many of which can be high in unhealthy fats and additives that may disrupt your digestion.

Fresh Over Processed: Whenever possible, choose fresh, whole foods over their processed counterparts. Fresh fruits, vegetables, and meats are more likely to be free of the additives that can cause digestive upset.

Reading Labels: A Decoder Ring for Your Diet

Learning to read food labels is akin to acquiring a decoder ring that unlocks the secrets of packaged foods. This skill is indispensable in making informed choices about what to put in your body.

Ingredient List: The ingredient list is your first line of defense. Look for short lists with ingredients you recognize as whole foods. Be wary of long lists with unpronounceable names, as these often indicate the presence of artificial additives and preservatives.

Hidden Fats: Post-gallbladder removal, your body's ability to process fats is altered. Pay close attention to the types and amounts of fat in foods. Watch out for hidden saturated and trans fats, often found in baked goods, snacks, and fried foods.

Fiber Content: Fiber plays a crucial role in your new diet. Look for foods with high dietary fiber, particularly soluble fiber, which can aid in digestion and help manage potential symptoms like diarrhea.

Sugar and Sodium: Excess sugar and sodium can contribute to various health issues. Keep an eye on their levels, especially in processed foods, where they can be surprisingly high.

Serving Size: Pay attention to serving sizes. What might seem like a reasonable amount of fat or sugar per serving can quickly become excessive if the serving size is smaller than you realize.

Navigating Dietary Restrictions with Confidence

Knowledge Is Power: Educate yourself about the specific dietary needs and restrictions post-gallbladder removal. This knowledge will empower you to make confident choices in the grocery store.

Avoiding Trigger Foods: Identify foods that tend to trigger your digestive symptoms and learn to spot them on labels. Common culprits can include high-fat foods, spicy foods, and certain dairy products.

Experiment and Adjust: Your body's responses to certain foods may change over time. Be open to experimenting with different foods and adjusting your diet as needed.

Seek Expert Advice: Don't hesitate to consult with a dietitian or nutritionist. They can provide tailored advice and help you navigate the complexities of grocery shopping and label reading, mastering the arts of grocery shopping and label reading is crucial in your journey post-gallbladder removal. These skills are not just about maintaining a diet; they're about embracing a lifestyle that prioritizes your health and well-being. With each thoughtful choice you make in the grocery store and each label you decode, you're taking a step towards a healthier, more informed way of living.

Chapter 4: Breakfasts to Start Your Day Right

Energizing Smoothie Bowls

RECIPE N: 1 Tropical Sunrise Smoothie Bowl

Preparation time: 10 minutes
Ingredients: Mango chunks, 1/2 cup; Pineapple pieces, 1/2 cup; Baby spinach, 1 cup; Low-fat Greek yogurt, 1/2 cup; Chia seeds, 1 tablespoon
Method of Cooking: Blender

Procedure: Blend mango, pineapple, spinach, and Greek yogurt until smooth, garnish with chia seeds
Nutritional values: High in Vitamin C, Protein, and Fiber
Servings: 1

RECIPE N: 2 Berry Almond Bliss Bowl

Preparation time: 10 minutes
Ingredients: Mixed berries, 1 cup; Almond milk, 1/2 cup; Rolled oats, 1/4 cup; Flaxseed, 1 tablespoon; Sliced almonds, 1 tablespoon
Method of Cooking: Blender
Procedure: Combine berries, almond milk, and oats in blender; blend until creamy; top with flaxseed and almonds
Nutritional values: Rich in Antioxidants, Omega-3, and Dietary Fiber
Servings: 1

RECIPE N: 3 Green Power Smoothie Bowl

Preparation time: 10 minutes
Ingredients: Kale leaves, 1 cup; Avocado, 1/2; Kiwi, 1; Coconut water, 1/2 cup; Hemp seeds, 1 tablespoon
Method of Cooking: Blender
Procedure: Puree kale, avocado, kiwi, and coconut water; sprinkle with hemp seeds
Nutritional values: Loaded with Vitamins A, C, and Healthy Fats
Servings: 1

RECIPE N: 4 Sunshine Citrus Bowl

Preparation time: 10 minutes
Ingredients: Orange segments, 1/2 cup; Carrot juice, 1/4 cup; Low-fat vanilla yogurt, 1/2 cup; Turmeric, 1/4 teaspoon; Pumpkin seeds, 1 tablespoon
Method of Cooking: Blender
Procedure: Blend orange, carrot juice, yogurt, and turmeric; top with pumpkin seeds
Nutritional values: High in Vitamin A, Probiotics, and Iron
Servings: 1

RECIPE N: 5 Red Velvet Beet Bowl

Preparation time: 10 minutes
Ingredients: Cooked beets, 1/2 cup; Raspberries, 1/2 cup; Low-fat cottage cheese, 1/2 cup; Cacao powder, 1 teaspoon; Unsweetened coconut, 1 tablespoon
Method of Cooking: Blender
Procedure: Blend beets, raspberries, cottage cheese, and cacao; sprinkle with coconut
Nutritional values: High in Protein, Fiber, and Antioxidants
Servings: 1

RECIPE N: 6 Peachy Green Bowl

Preparation time: 10 minutes
Ingredients: Peach slices, 1/2 cup; Spinach, 1 cup; Low-fat kefir, 1/2 cup; Ground ginger, 1/4 teaspoon; Sunflower seeds, 1 tablespoon
Method of Cooking: Blender
Procedure: Combine peach, spinach, kefir, and ginger; blend smoothly; garnish with sunflower seeds
Nutritional values: Rich in Calcium, Vitamin K, and Probiotics
Servings: 1

RECIPE N: 7 Zesty Blueberry Bowl

Preparation time: 10 minutes
Ingredients: Blueberries, 1/2 cup; Lemon zest, 1 teaspoon; Low-fat Greek yogurt, 1/2 cup; Granola, 2 tablespoons; Honey, 1 teaspoon
Method of Cooking: Blender

Procedure: Blend blueberries, lemon zest, and yogurt; top with granola and a drizzle of honey
Nutritional values: Rich in Vitamin C, Protein, and Whole Grains
Servings: 1

RECIPE N: 8 Tropical Avocado Bowl

Preparation time: 10 minutes
Ingredients: Avocado, 1/2; Pineapple chunks, 1/2 cup; Coconut milk, 1/4 cup; Lime juice, 1 tablespoon; Toasted coconut flakes, 1 tablespoon
Method of Cooking: Blender

Procedure: Blend avocado, pineapple, coconut milk, and lime juice; top with toasted coconut
Nutritional values: High in Healthy Fats, Vitamin C, and Fiber
Servings: 1

RECIPE N: 9 Spiced Pear Oat Bowl

Preparation time: 10 minutes
Ingredients: Pear slices, 1/2 cup; Rolled oats, 1/4 cup; Almond milk, 1/2 cup; Cinnamon, 1/4 teaspoon; Walnuts, 1 tablespoon
Method of Cooking: Blender

Procedure: Combine pear, oats, almond milk, and cinnamon; blend until smooth; garnish with walnuts
Nutritional values: High in Fiber, Vitamin E, and Heart-Healthy Fats
Servings: 1

RECIPE N: 10 Antioxidant Acai Bowl

Preparation time: 10 minutes
Ingredients: Acai berry puree, 1/2 cup; Banana, 1/2; Low-fat Greek yogurt, 1/2 cup; Honey, 1 teaspoon; Mixed berries, 1/4 cup
Method of Cooking: Blender

Procedure: Blend acai puree, banana, and yogurt; top with honey and mixed berries
Nutritional values: Packed with Antioxidants, Potassium, and Protein
Servings: 1

Low-Fat Omelettes and Scrambles

RECIPE N: 1 Mediterranean Veggie Scramble

Preparation time: 15 minutes
Ingredients: Egg whites, 4; Spinach, 1 cup; Cherry tomatoes, 1/2 cup; Feta cheese, 1/4 cup; Olive oil, 1 teaspoon
Method of Cooking: Skillet
Procedure: Sauté spinach and tomatoes in olive oil, add egg whites, scramble gently, top with feta
Nutritional values: High in Protein, Low in Fat, Rich in Vitamins A and C
Servings: 1

RECIPE N: 2 Herbed Mushroom Omelette

Preparation time: 15 minutes
Ingredients: Egg whites, 3; Sliced mushrooms, 1/2 cup; Fresh herbs (parsley, chives), 1 tablespoon; Low-fat cheese, 1/4 cup; Olive oil, 1 teaspoon
Method of Cooking: Skillet
Procedure: Cook mushrooms in olive oil, pour egg whites over, sprinkle herbs and cheese, fold omelet
Nutritional values: Rich in Protein, Low in Calories, Source of Antioxidants
Servings: 1

RECIPE N: 3 Spinach and Goat Cheese Scramble

Preparation time: 15 minutes
Ingredients: Egg whites, 3; Baby spinach, 1 cup; Goat cheese, 2 tablespoons; Black pepper, to taste; Olive oil, 1 teaspoon
Method of Cooking: Skillet

Procedure: Sauté spinach in olive oil, add egg whites and scramble, mix in goat cheese and pepper
Nutritional values: High in Iron, Protein, and Calcium
Servings: 1

RECIPE N: 4 Tomato Basil Frittata

Preparation time: 20 minutes
Ingredients: Whole eggs, 2; Egg whites, 2; Cherry tomatoes, 1/2 cup; Fresh basil, 1 tablespoon; Low-fat mozzarella, 1/4 cup
Method of Cooking: Oven

Procedure: Whisk eggs and egg whites, add tomatoes and basil, bake, top with mozzarella
Nutritional values: Rich in Protein, Vitamins A and C, and Calcium
Servings: 2

RECIPE N: 5 Zucchini and Bell Pepper Mini Quiches

Preparation time: 25 minutes
Ingredients: Egg whites, 6; Grated zucchini, 1/2 cup; Diced bell pepper, 1/2 cup; Low-fat cheddar, 1/4 cup; Salt and pepper, to taste
Method of Cooking: Oven, muffin tin

Procedure: Mix egg whites with vegetables, pour into muffin tin, top with cheese, bake until set
Nutritional values: Low in Fat, High in Protein and Fiber
Servings: 6 mini quiches

RECIPE N: 6 Asparagus and Parmesan Omelette

Preparation time: 15 minutes
Ingredients: Egg whites, 3; Chopped asparagus, 1/2 cup; Grated Parmesan cheese, 2 tablespoons; Olive oil, 1 teaspoon; Salt and pepper, to taste
Method of Cooking: Skillet

Procedure: Sauté asparagus in olive oil, add egg whites, sprinkle Parmesan, salt, and pepper, fold omelet
Nutritional values: High in Protein, Vitamins A, C, and K
Servings: 1

RECIPE N: 7 Smoked Salmon Scramble

Preparation time: 15 minutes
Ingredients: Egg whites, 3; Smoked salmon, 2 ounces; Capers, 1 tablespoon; Dill, 1 teaspoon; Low-fat cream cheese, 1 tablespoon
Method of Cooking: Skillet

Procedure: Scramble egg whites, add salmon, capers, and dill, dollop with cream cheese
Nutritional values: High in Omega-3 Fatty Acids, Protein, and Low in Fat
Servings: 1

RECIPE N: 8 Sweet Potato and Kale Frittata

Preparation time: 20 minutes
Ingredients: Whole eggs, 2; Egg whites, 2; Diced sweet potato, 1/2 cup; Chopped kale, 1 cup; Low-fat feta cheese, 1/4 cup
Method of Cooking: Oven
Procedure: Whisk eggs, mix with sweet potato and kale, bake, sprinkle with feta
Nutritional values: Rich in Beta-Carotene, Vitamins C and K, and Protein
Servings: 2

RECIPE N: 9 Avocado and Egg White Wrap

Preparation time: 15 minutes
Ingredients: Egg whites, 3; Whole wheat tortilla, 1; Sliced avocado, 1/2; Salsa, 2 tablespoons; Lime juice, 1 teaspoon
Method of Cooking: Skillet, Microwave

Procedure: Scramble egg whites, warm tortilla, fill with eggs, avocado, salsa, and lime
Nutritional values: High in Protein, Fiber, and Healthy Fats
Servings: 1

RECIPE N: 10 Bell Pepper and Onion Frittata Muffins

Preparation time: 25 minutes
Ingredients: Egg whites, 6; Diced bell pepper, 1/2 cup; Chopped onion, 1/4 cup; Low-fat mozzarella, 1/4 cup; Garlic powder, 1/2 teaspoon
Method of Cooking: Oven, muffin tin

Procedure: Mix egg whites with bell pepper and onion, pour into muffin tin, top with cheese, bake
Nutritional values: Low in Calories, High in Protein and Vitamin C
Servings: 6 mini frittatas

Wholesome Porridge and Grains

RECIPE N° 1: Sunrise Berry Smoothie Bowl

Preparation time: 10 minutes
Ingredients: Frozen mixed berries 100g, Almond milk 200ml, Chia seeds 2 tbsp, Sunflower kernels 1 tbsp, Pure maple syrup 1 tsp
Method of Cooking: Blend until smooth

Procedure: Combine berries, almond milk, and maple syrup in a blender; blend until creamy. Top with chia seeds and sunflower kernels.
Nutritional Values: Rich in antioxidants, low in fat
Servings: 1

RECIPE N° 2: Mediterranean Herb Omelette

Preparation time: 15 minutes
Ingredients: Egg whites 3, Spinach 50g, Cherry tomatoes 5, halved, Feta cheese 30g, crumbled, Oregano 1 tsp
Method of Cooking: Sauté and fold
Procedure: Whisk egg whites; sauté spinach and tomatoes in a non-stick pan; pour in eggs, sprinkle with oregano and feta; cook until set; fold.
Nutritional Values: High in protein, low in cholesterol
Servings: 1

RECIPE N° 3: Apple Cinnamon Quinoa Porridge

Preparation time: 20 minutes
Ingredients: Quinoa 50g, Almond milk 250ml, chopped apple 1, Cinnamon 1 tsp, Almond slivers 1 tbsp
Method of Cooking: Simmer and stir
Procedure: Cook quinoa in almond milk, add chopped apple and cinnamon halfway through; simmer until creamy; top with almond slivers.
Nutritional Values: High fiber, plant-based protein
Servings: 1

RECIPE N° 4: Tropical Bliss Smoothie Bowl

Preparation time: 10 minutes
Ingredients: Frozen mango 100g, Coconut milk 200ml, Toasted coconut flakes 1 tbsp, Pumpkin seeds 1 tbsp, Honey 1 tsp
Method of Cooking: Blend smoothly
Procedure: Blend mango and coconut milk until smooth; garnish with toasted coconut flakes and pumpkin seeds, drizzle with honey.
Nutritional Values: Vitamin-rich, dairy-free
Servings: 1

RECIPE N° 5: Spinach and Mushroom Scramble

Preparation time: 15 minutes
Ingredients: Egg whites 4, Sliced mushrooms 50g, Spinach 60g, Olive oil 1 tsp, Thyme 1/2 tsp
Method of Cooking: Sauté and scramble
Procedure: Sauté mushrooms in olive oil, add spinach; whisk in egg whites and thyme; cook until scrambled.
Nutritional Values: Low fat, rich in iron
Servings: 1

RECIPE N° 6: Peachy Keen Steel-Cut Oats

Preparation time: 25 minutes
Ingredients: Steel-cut oats 50g, sliced peaches 1 peach, Almond milk 300ml, Cinnamon 1 tsp, Walnut pieces 1 tbsp
Method of Cooking: Simmer and stir
Procedure: Cook steel-cut oats in almond milk with cinnamon; when almost done, stir in peach slices; serve topped with walnut pieces.
Nutritional Values: High in fiber, vitamin C
Servings: 1

RECIPE N° 7: Avocado and Tomato Scramble

Preparation time: 15 minutes
Ingredients: Egg whites 3, Ripe avocado 1/2, diced, Cherry tomatoes 6, halved, Fresh basil 1 tsp, chopped, Black pepper to taste
Method of Cooking: Scramble and fold
Procedure: Whisk egg whites; pour into a hot non-stick pan; halfway through cooking, add avocado, tomatoes, and basil; season with pepper.
Nutritional Values: Rich in healthy fats, low in sodium
Servings: 1

RECIPE N° 8: Berry Almond Overnight Oats

Preparation time: Overnight + 5 minutes
Ingredients: Rolled oats 50g, Greek yogurt 100g, Mixed berries 100g, Almond milk 150ml, sliced almonds 1 tbsp
Method of Cooking: No cook, refrigerate
Procedure: Mix oats, yogurt, almond milk, and half of the berries; refrigerate overnight; top with remaining berries and almonds before serving.
Nutritional Values: High in protein, probiotics
Servings: 1

RECIPE N° 9: Green Goddess Smoothie Bowl

Preparation time: 10 minutes
Ingredients: Spinach 1 cup, Frozen banana 1, Avocado 1/2, Spirulina powder 1 tsp, Hemp seeds 1 tbsp, Almond milk 200ml
Method of Cooking: Blend until smooth
Procedure: Blend spinach, banana, avocado, spirulina, and almond milk until creamy; top with hemp seeds.
Nutritional Values: Rich in antioxidants, omega-3 fatty acids
Servings: 1

RECIPE N° 10: Savory Veggie Breakfast Bowl

Preparation time: 20 minutes
Ingredients: Quinoa 50g, Baby spinach 1 cup, Cherry tomatoes 10, halved, Bell pepper 1/2, diced, Olive oil 1 tsp, Lemon juice 1 tsp
Method of Cooking: Sauté and assemble
Procedure: Cook quinoa as directed; sauté spinach, tomatoes, and bell pepper in olive oil; combine with quinoa; drizzle with lemon juice.
Nutritional Values: Rich in vitamins, plant-based.**Servings** : 1

34

Chapter 5: Light and Nutritious Lunches

Fresh and Crunchy Salads

RECIPE N° 1: Garden Fresh Quinoa Salad

Preparation time: 20 minutes
Ingredients: Quinoa 50g, Baby spinach leaves 1 cup, Cherry tomatoes 10, halved, Cucumber 1/2, diced, red onion 1/4, thinly sliced, Lemon juice 2 tbsp
Method of Cooking: Toss and chill

Procedure: Cook quinoa, let cool; combine with spinach, tomatoes, cucumber, onion; dress with lemon juice; refrigerate before serving.
Nutritional values: High in fiber, vitamin-rich
Servings: 2

RECIPE N° 2: Crunchy Rainbow Slaw

Preparation time: 15 minutes
Ingredients: Red cabbage 1/2 cup, shredded, Carrots 2, julienned, Bell pepper 1, thinly sliced, Apple cider vinegar 1 tbsp, Olive oil 1 tsp, Honey 1 tsp
Method of Cooking: Mix and marinate

Procedure: Toss cabbage, carrots, bell pepper; whisk vinegar, oil, honey; pour over slaw; let marinate for 1 hour.
Nutritional values: Antioxidant-rich, low calorie
Servings: 2

RECIPE N° 3: Mediterranean Chickpea Salad

Preparation time: 15 minutes
Ingredients: Chickpeas 1 can, drained, Cucumber 1, diced, Cherry tomatoes 1 cup, halved, Feta cheese 50g, crumbled, Parsley 1 tbsp, chopped, Lemon juice 2 tbsp
Method of Cooking: Combine and chill

Procedure: Mix chickpeas, cucumber, tomatoes, feta, parsley; dress with lemon juice; refrigerate for flavors to meld.
Nutritional values: High in protein, fiber-rich
Servings: 2

RECIPE N° 4: Avocado and Black Bean Salad

Preparation time: 20 minutes
Ingredients: Black beans 1 can, drained, Avocado 1, diced, Corn kernels 1/2 cup, red onion 1/4 cup, finely chopped, Cilantro 1 tbsp, chopped, Lime juice 2 tbsp
Method of Cooking: Toss gently

Procedure: Combine black beans, avocado, corn, onion, cilantro; gently mix with lime juice; serve chilled.
Nutritional values: Rich in healthy fats, fiber
Servings: 2

RECIPE N° 5: Asian Sesame Tofu Salad

Preparation time: 25 minutes
Ingredients: Firm tofu 200g, cubed, Mixed greens 2 cups, Carrot 1, shredded, red bell pepper 1/2, sliced, Sesame seeds 1 tbsp, Soy sauce 2 tbsp, Sesame oil 1 tsp
Method of Cooking: Sauté and assemble

Procedure: Sauté tofu in sesame oil until golden; toss with greens, carrot, bell pepper; sprinkle with sesame seeds, soy sauce.
Nutritional values: High in plant protein, low in fat
Servings: 2

RECIPE N° 6: Pear and Walnut Arugula Salad

Preparation time: 15 minutes
Ingredients: Arugula 2 cups, Pear 1, thinly sliced, Walnuts 1/4 cup, crumbled, blue cheese 30g, crumbled, Balsamic vinegar 2 tbsp, Extra-virgin olive oil 1 tbsp
Method of Cooking: Toss and serve

Procedure: Combine arugula, pear slices, walnuts, and blue cheese; drizzle with balsamic vinegar and olive oil before serving.
Nutritional values: Rich in healthy fats, antioxidants
Servings: 2

RECIPE N° 7: Zesty Lentil and Beet Salad

Preparation time: 30 minutes
Ingredients: Cooked lentils 1 cup, Beetroot 1, cooked and diced, Spinach leaves 1 cup, Goat cheese 30g, crumbled, orange juice 2 tbsp, Olive oil 1 tsp
Method of Cooking: Mix and chill

Procedure: Toss lentils, beetroot, and spinach; top with goat cheese; dress with a mix of orange juice and olive oil; refrigerate briefly.
Nutritional values: High in fiber, iron
Servings: 2

RECIPE N° 8: Spiced Chickpea and Quinoa Bowl

Preparation time: 25 minutes
Ingredients: Quinoa 50g, Cooked chickpeas 1 cup, Spinach 1 cup, Cumin powder 1/2 tsp, Olive oil 1 tbsp, Lemon juice 1 tbsp
Method of Cooking: Sauté and combine

Procedure: Cook quinoa; separately, sauté chickpeas with cumin in olive oil; mix with quinoa and spinach; dress with lemon juice.
Nutritional values: Protein-rich, high in vitamins
Servings: 2

RECIPE N° 9: Summer Berry Spinach Salad

Preparation time: 15 minutes
Ingredients: Spinach 2 cups, Strawberries 1 cup, sliced, Blueberries 1/2 cup, Almonds 1/4 cup, sliced, Feta cheese 50g, crumbled, Balsamic glaze 1 tbsp
Method of Cooking: Toss and drizzle

Procedure: Combine spinach, strawberries, blueberries, almonds, and feta; drizzle with balsamic glaze just before serving.
Nutritional values: Vitamin C-rich, fiber
Servings: 2

RECIPE N° 10: Grilled Veggie and Hummus Wrap

Preparation time: 20 minutes
Ingredients: Whole wheat wraps 2, Hummus 4 tbsp, Zucchini 1, thinly sliced, Bell pepper 1, sliced, red onion 1/4, sliced, Olive oil 1 tsp
Method of Cooking: Grill and roll
Procedure: Grill zucchini, bell pepper, and onion in olive oil; spread hummus on wraps; add grilled veggies; roll up tightly.
Nutritional values: High in fiber, plant-based
Servings: 2

Hearty Soups and Broths

RECIPE N° 1: Velvet Butternut Squash Soup

Preparation time: 35 minutes
Ingredients: Butternut squash 1, peeled and cubed, Vegetable broth 4 cups, Onion 1, diced, Garlic cloves 2, minced, Nutmeg pinch, Olive oil 1 tbsp
Method of Cooking: Simmer and blend

Procedure: Sauté onion and garlic in olive oil; add squash, broth, nutmeg; simmer until tender; blend until smooth.
Nutritional values: High in vitamins A and C
Servings: 4

RECIPE N° 2: Classic Lentil Soup

Preparation time: 45 minutes
Ingredients: Dried lentils 1 cup, Carrots 2, diced, Celery stalks 2, diced, Tomato 1, diced, Vegetable broth 6 cups, Thyme 1 tsp
Method of Cooking: Simmer and stir

Procedure: Combine lentils, carrots, celery, tomato, broth, thyme in a pot; simmer until lentils are tender.
Nutritional values: Rich in protein and fiber
Servings: 4

RECIPE N° 3: Tomato Basil Bisque

Preparation time: 30 minutes
Ingredients: Canned tomatoes 28 oz, Basil leaves 1/4 cup, chopped, Onion 1, diced, Garlic clove 1, minced, Vegetable broth 3 cups, Olive oil 1 tbsp
Method of Cooking: Sauté and blend

Procedure: Sauté onion, garlic in olive oil; add tomatoes, broth; simmer; add basil; blend until creamy.
Nutritional values: High in lycopene and vitamin C
Servings: 4

RECIPE N° 4: Garden Vegetable Broth

Preparation time: 1 hour
Ingredients: Assorted vegetables (carrots, onions, celery) chopped, 4 cups, Garlic cloves 3, Bay leaves 2, Peppercorns 1 tsp, Water 8 cups
Method of Cooking: Simmer and strain

Procedure: Combine all ingredients in a large pot; simmer for an hour; strain to obtain clear broth.
Nutritional values: Low calorie, hydrating
Servings: 6

RECIPE N° 5: Spicy Black Bean Soup

Preparation time: 40 minutes
Ingredients: Black beans 2 cans, drained, Onion 1, diced, Garlic cloves 2, minced, Cumin 1 tsp, Vegetable broth 4 cups, Jalapeño 1, diced
Method of Cooking: Sauté, simmer, and blend

Procedure: Sauté onion, garlic, jalapeño; add beans, cumin, broth; simmer; blend some beans for thickness.
Nutritional values: High in fiber and protein
Servings: 4

RECIPE N: 6 - Spicy Black Bean Soup

Preparation Time: 30 minutes
Ingredients: Black beans (2 cups, cooked), Onion (1, medium), Garlic (3 cloves), Vegetable broth (4 cups), Cumin (1 tsp), Chili powder (1 tsp), Olive oil (1 tbsp), Diced tomatoes (1 cup), Lime juice (1 tbsp)
Method of Cooking: Boiling and Blending

Procedure: Sauté onion and garlic in olive oil, add beans, tomatoes, cumin, chili powder, pour in broth, boil and simmer for 20 minutes, blend partially, add lime juice.
Nutritional Values: High in fiber, protein, and antioxidants.
Servings: 4

RECIPE N: 7 - Sweet Potato and Red Lentil Soup

Preparation Time: 40 minutes
Ingredients: Sweet potatoes (2, medium-sized), Red lentils (1 cup), Onion (1, medium), Vegetable broth (5 cups), Ginger (1 inch), Turmeric (1/2 tsp), Coconut milk (1 cup), Olive oil (1 tbsp), Salt and pepper (to taste)
Method of Cooking: Simmering

Procedure: Sauté onion and ginger in olive oil, add cubed sweet potatoes, lentils, turmeric, pour in broth, simmer until lentils and potatoes are tender, blend until smooth, stir in coconut milk.
Nutritional Values: Rich in beta-carotene, vitamins, and dietary fiber.
Servings: 4

RECIPE N: 8 - Classic Minestrone Soup

Preparation Time: 45 minutes
Ingredients: Carrots (2), Celery stalks (2), Onion (1, medium), Garlic (3 cloves), Diced tomatoes (1 can), Vegetable broth (6 cups), Cannellini beans (1 cup, cooked), Green beans (1 cup, chopped), Zucchini (1), Pasta (1/2 cup), Olive oil (1 tbsp), Salt and pepper (to taste), Fresh parsley (1/4 cup)
Method of Cooking: Boiling

Procedure: Sauté carrots, celery, onion, and garlic in olive oil, add tomatoes, broth, beans, pasta, green beans, zucchini, boil and simmer until vegetables and pasta are tender, season with salt, pepper, garnish with parsley.
Nutritional Values: Loaded with vegetables, providing a variety of vitamins and minerals.
Servings: 5

RECIPE N: 9 - Roasted Red Pepper and Tomato Soup

Preparation Time: 30 minutes
Ingredients: Roasted red peppers (1 cup), Tomatoes (3, large), Onion (1, small), Vegetable broth (4 cups), Garlic (2 cloves), Basil (1 tbsp), Olive oil (1 tbsp), Salt (to taste), Pepper (to taste), Cream (optional, for serving)
Method of Cooking: Roasting and Blending

Procedure: Roast peppers and tomatoes, sauté onion and garlic in olive oil, blend all with broth and basil until smooth, reheat, season with salt and pepper, serve with a swirl of cream if desired.
Nutritional Values: High in vitamin C and antioxidants.
Servings: 4

RECIPE N: 10 - Barley and Vegetable Soup

Preparation Time: 50 minutes
Ingredients: Barley (1/2 cup), Carrots (2), Celery stalks (2), Onion (1, medium), Vegetable broth (6 cups), Garlic (2 cloves), Olive oil (1 tbsp), Diced tomatoes (1 cup), Spinach (2 cups), Salt and pepper (to taste)
Method of Cooking: Simmering

Procedure: Sauté onion, carrots, celery, and garlic in olive oil, add barley, tomatoes, pour in broth, simmer until barley is tender, stir in spinach, season with salt and pepper.
Nutritional Values: Good source of dietary fiber and essential nutrients.
Servings: 4

Wraps and Sandwiches with a Healthy Twist

RECIPE N: 1 - Avocado and Chickpea Hummus Wrap

Preparation Time: 15 minutes
Ingredients: Chickpeas (1 cup), Avocado (1), Whole wheat tortilla (1), Baby spinach (1 handful), Red bell pepper (½), Lemon juice (1 tbsp), Tahini (2 tsp), Garlic (1 clove), Cumin (½ tsp), Olive oil (1 tsp)
Cooking Method: No cooking required

Procedure: Blend chickpeas, avocado, lemon juice, tahini, minced garlic, cumin, and olive oil to create a creamy spread. Apply evenly onto the tortilla, add spinach and sliced bell pepper, then roll.
Nutritional Values: A blend of fiber, healthy fats, and plant protein.
Servings: 1

RECIPE N: 2 - Mediterranean Veggie Pita Pocket

Preparation Time: 10 minutes

Ingredients: Whole wheat pita (1), Hummus (2 tbsp), Cucumber (¼), Tomato (1), Kalamata olives (¼ cup), Feta cheese, crumbled (1 tbsp), Red onion, thinly sliced (1 tbsp), Baby arugula (1 handful)

Cooking Method: No cooking required

Procedure: Cut the pita into halves to form pockets. Inside each, layer hummus, cucumber slices, tomato pieces, olives, feta, onion, and arugula.

Nutritional Values: Rich in essential vitamins, minerals, and healthy fats.

Servings: 1

RECIPE N: 3 - Tofu Lettuce Wraps

Preparation Time: 20 minutes

Ingredients: Firm tofu (½ block), Butter lettuce (8 leaves), Carrot, shredded (½ cup), Red cabbage, shredded (½ cup), Low sodium soy sauce (2 tbsp), Sesame oil (1 tsp), Grated ginger (1 tsp), Minced garlic (1 clove), Chopped green onion (1 tbsp), Sesame seeds (1 tsp)

Cooking Method: Pan-frying

Procedure: Compress tofu to remove excess moisture, then dice. Sauté in a pan with sesame oil, garlic, and ginger until browned. Add soy sauce, stir for 2 more minutes. Place tofu mix in lettuce leaves, garnish with carrot, cabbage, green onion, and sesame seeds.

Nutritional Values: High in protein, fiber, and vitamins.

Servings: 2

RECIPE N: 4 - Grilled Vegetable and Hummus Sandwich

Preparation Time: 25 minutes

Ingredients: Whole grain bread (2 slices), Hummus (3 tbsp), Zucchini, sliced (½), Red bell pepper (1), Eggplant, sliced (½ cup), Olive oil (1 tsp), Balsamic vinegar (1 tsp), Salt and pepper (to taste), Arugula (½ cup)

Cooking Method: Grilling

Procedure: Marinate zucchini, bell pepper, and eggplant in olive oil and vinegar, season with salt and pepper, and grill until tender. Spread hummus on one bread slice, layer on vegetables and arugula, top with the second slice.

Nutritional Values: High in dietary fiber, vitamins, and plant-based nutrients.

Servings: 1

RECIPE N: 5 - Quinoa and Black Bean Burrito

Preparation Time: 30 minutes
Ingredients: Cooked quinoa (1 cup), Black beans (½ cup), Whole wheat tortilla (1), Avocado, sliced (½), Salsa (2 tbsp), Lime juice (1 tsp), Chopped cilantro (1 tbsp), Minced red onion (1 tbsp), Cumin (½ tsp), Salt and pepper (to taste)
Cooking Method: Mixing

Procedure: Mix together quinoa, black beans, lime juice, cilantro, red onion, cumin, salt, and pepper. Spread this blend onto the tortilla, layer with avocado and salsa, then roll it up.
Nutritional Values: Rich in plant-based proteins and essential amino acids.
Servings: 1

RECIPE N 6: Smoked Salmon and Avocado Toast

Preparation time: 5 minutes
Ingredients: 2 slices of whole-grain bread, toasted; 4 oz smoked salmon; 1 ripe avocado, sliced; 1 tbsp capers; 1 tsp lemon juice; pinch of dill
Cooking method: Toasting
Procedure: Layer the avocado slices on toasted bread, top with smoked salmon, sprinkle capers, dill, and a dash of lemon juice.
Nutritional values: Rich in omega-3 fatty acids, protein, and healthy fats
Servings: 2

RECIPE N 7: Pesto Chicken Salad Wrap

Preparation time: 20 minutes
Ingredients: 1 grilled chicken breast, diced; 2 tbsp basil pesto; 1 cup mixed greens; ½ cup cherry tomatoes, halved; 1 whole wheat wrap
Cooking method: Grilling and assembly

Procedure: Toss diced chicken with pesto, mix in greens and tomatoes. Place mixture in the center of the wrap, fold and serve.
Nutritional values: High in protein, vitamins A and C
Servings: 1

RECIPE N 8 : Spicy Black Bean Burrito

Preparation time: 15 minutes
Ingredients: 1 cup canned black beans, rinsed and drained; 1 whole wheat tortilla; ¼ cup brown rice, cooked; 2 tbsp salsa; 2 tbsp Greek yogurt; 1 tbsp jalapeños, chopped
Cooking method: Microwave and assembly

Procedure: Warm beans and rice, spread on tortilla, add salsa, jalapeños, and a dollop of Greek yogurt, roll into a burrito.
Nutritional values: Rich in fiber and plant-based protein
Servings: 1

RECIPE N 9: Curried Egg Salad Sandwich

Preparation time: 10 minutes
Ingredients: 2 hard-boiled eggs, chopped; 2 tbsp Greek yogurt; ½ tsp curry powder; 2 slices multigrain bread; lettuce leaves; salt to taste
Cooking method: Boiling and assembly

Procedure: Mix eggs, yogurt, curry powder, and salt. Spread on bread, add lettuce, top with the second slice.
Nutritional values: Good source of protein and low in fat
Servings: 1

RECIPE N 10: Roast Beef and Horseradish Cream Cheese Roll-Up

Preparation time: 5 minutes
Ingredients: 3 oz lean roast beef slices; 2 tbsp cream cheese with horseradish; 1 whole wheat tortilla; ¼ cup arugula
Cooking method: Assembly
Procedure: Spread cream cheese on tortilla, lay down arugula, add roast beef on top, roll tightly, and slice into rounds.
Nutritional values: High in protein and contains iron
Servings: 1

Chapter 6: Satisfying Dinner Recipes

Lean Protein Dishes

RECIPE N: 1 - Grilled Chicken with Herb Quinoa

Preparation Time: 30 minutes
Ingredients: Chicken breast (6 oz), Quinoa (1 cup), Olive oil (1 tbsp), Lemon juice (2 tbsp), Garlic (1 clove), Rosemary (1 tsp), Thyme (1 tsp), Salt (to taste), Pepper (to taste)
Method of Cooking: Grilling and Boiling

Procedure: Marinate chicken in olive oil, lemon juice, minced garlic, rosemary, thyme, salt, and pepper, then grill until fully cooked; simultaneously, boil quinoa as per instructions, mix with remaining herbs.
Nutritional Values: High in lean protein and whole grains.
Servings: 1

RECIPE N: 2 - Baked Salmon with Asparagus

Preparation Time: 25 minutes
Ingredients: Salmon fillet (6 oz), Asparagus (1 bunch), Lemon (1), Dill (1 tsp), Olive oil (1 tbsp), Garlic powder (1/2 tsp), Salt (to taste), Pepper (to taste)
Method of Cooking: Baking

Procedure: Place salmon and asparagus on a baking sheet, drizzle with olive oil, season with dill, garlic powder, salt, pepper, and lemon slices, bake at 375°F until salmon is flaky.
Nutritional Values: Rich in omega-3 fatty acids and vitamins.
Servings: 1

RECIPE N: 3 - Turkey and Spinach Stuffed Bell Peppers

Preparation Time: 45 minutes
Ingredients: Bell peppers (2), Ground turkey (1/2 lb), Spinach (1 cup), Onion (1, small), Garlic (1 clove), Tomato sauce (1/2 cup), Cumin (1 tsp), Olive oil (1 tbsp), Salt and pepper (to taste)
Method of Cooking: Baking and Sautéing

Procedure: Sauté onion, garlic, and ground turkey in olive oil, add spinach, tomato sauce, cumin, salt, and pepper; stuff this mixture into halved and deseeded bell peppers, bake at 350°F for 25 minutes.
Nutritional Values: A great source of lean protein and iron.
Servings: 2

RECIPE N: 4 - Lemon Garlic Shrimp Skewers

Preparation Time: 20 minutes
Ingredients: Shrimp (8 oz), Lemon juice (2 tbsp), Garlic (2 cloves), Olive oil (1 tbsp), Paprika (1/2 tsp), Salt (to taste), Pepper (to taste), Skewers (4)
Method of Cooking: Grilling

Procedure: Marinate shrimp in lemon juice, minced garlic, olive oil, paprika, salt, and pepper; thread onto skewers; grill each side for about 2-3 minutes or until shrimp are pink and opaque.
Nutritional Values: High in protein and low in fat.
Servings: 2

RECIPE N: 5 - Seared Tuna Steaks with Ginger Soy Glaze

Preparation Time: 20 minutes
Ingredients: Tuna steaks (2, 6 oz each), Soy sauce (2 tbsp), Ginger (1 inch), Honey (1 tbsp), Sesame oil (1 tsp), Garlic (1 clove), Scallions (2, chopped), Sesame seeds (1 tsp)
Method of Cooking: Searing

Procedure: Mix soy sauce, grated ginger, honey, minced garlic for glaze; sear tuna steaks in sesame oil, about 2 minutes per side for medium-rare; glaze with the soy mixture, garnish with scallions and sesame seeds.

Nutritional Values: Rich in omega-3s and lean protein.
Servings: 2

RECIPE N: 6 - Herb-Crusted Cod with Zucchini Noodles

Preparation Time: 25 minutes
Ingredients: Cod fillets (2, 6 oz each), Zucchini (2, spiralized), Parsley (2 tbsp, chopped), Lemon zest (1 tsp), Garlic powder (1/2 tsp), Olive oil (2 tbsp), Salt (to taste), Pepper (to taste)
Method of Cooking: Baking and Sautéing

Procedure: Coat cod with parsley, lemon zest, garlic powder, salt, pepper, bake at 375°F until flaky; sauté spiralized zucchini in olive oil until tender.
Nutritional Values: High in protein and low in carbohydrates.
Servings: 2

RECIPE N: 7 - Grilled Pork Tenderloin with Apple Salsa

Preparation Time: 35 minutes
Ingredients: Pork tenderloin (1 lb), Apples (2, diced), Red onion (1/4 cup, diced), Cilantro (2 tbsp, chopped), Lime juice (2 tbsp), Chili powder (1 tsp), Olive oil (1 tbsp), Salt and pepper (to taste)
Method of Cooking: Grilling

Procedure: Season pork with salt, pepper, chili powder, grill until internal temperature reaches 145°F; mix apples, onion, cilantro, lime juice for salsa; serve pork sliced with apple salsa on top.
Nutritional Values: Good source of lean protein and vitamins.
Servings: 4

RECIPE N: 8 - Balsamic Glazed Chicken Breast

Preparation Time: 30 minutes
Ingredients: Chicken breasts (2, 6 oz each), Balsamic vinegar (1/4 cup), Honey (1 tbsp), Garlic (1 clove, minced), Rosemary (1 tsp), Olive oil (1 tbsp), Salt (to taste), Pepper (to taste)
Method of Cooking: Sautéing

Procedure: Marinate chicken in balsamic vinegar, honey, garlic, rosemary, salt, pepper; sauté in olive oil until cooked through, let the marinade reduce to a glaze.
Nutritional Values: High in protein and rich in flavors.
Servings: 2

RECIPE N: 9 - Spiced Turkey Meatballs with Tomato Sauce

Preparation Time: 45 minutes
Ingredients: Ground turkey (1 lb), Onion (1/2 cup, finely chopped), Garlic (2 cloves, minced), Cumin (1 tsp), Paprika (1 tsp), Tomato sauce (1 cup), Olive oil (1 tbsp), Salt and pepper (to taste)
Method of Cooking: Baking

Procedure: Mix turkey with onion, garlic, cumin, paprika, salt, pepper; form into meatballs; bake at 375°F for 20 minutes; simmer in tomato sauce.
Nutritional Values: Excellent source of lean protein and spices.
Servings: 4

RECIPE N: 10 - Garlic Lime Flank Steak

Preparation Time: 25 minutes + Marinating
Ingredients: Flank steak (1 lb), Garlic (3 cloves, minced), Lime juice (1/4 cup), Soy sauce (2 tbsp), Honey (1 tbsp), Olive oil (2 tbsp), Cilantro (1/4 cup, chopped), Salt and pepper (to taste)
Method of Cooking: Grilling

Procedure: Marinate steak in garlic, lime juice, soy sauce, honey, olive oil, salt, pepper; grill to desired doneness; rest for 5 minutes, slice against the grain, garnish with cilantro.
Nutritional Values: Rich in protein and zesty flavors.
Servings: 4

Vegetarian Delights

RECIPE N: 1 - Stuffed Portobello Mushrooms

Preparation Time: 30 minutes
Ingredients: Portobello mushrooms (4), Quinoa (1 cup, cooked), Spinach (2 cups), Garlic (2 cloves, minced), Feta cheese (1/2 cup, crumbled), Cherry tomatoes (1 cup, halved), Olive oil (2 tbsp), Balsamic vinegar (1 tbsp), Salt and pepper (to taste)
Method of Cooking: Baking

Procedure: Sauté spinach and garlic in olive oil, mix with quinoa, feta, tomatoes, stuff into mushroom caps, drizzle with balsamic, bake at 375°F until tender.
Nutritional Values: High in protein, fiber, and vitamins.
Servings: 4

RECIPE N: 2 - Creamy Avocado Pasta

Preparation Time: 20 minutes
Ingredients: Whole wheat pasta (8 oz), Avocado (1, ripe), Garlic (1 clove), Lemon juice (2 tbsp), Olive oil (1 tbsp), Cherry tomatoes (1 cup, halved), Basil leaves (1/4 cup), Salt and pepper (to taste)
Method of Cooking: Boiling and Blending

Procedure: Cook pasta, blend avocado with garlic, lemon juice, olive oil for sauce, toss pasta with sauce, tomatoes, basil, season with salt and pepper.
Nutritional Values: Rich in healthy fats and fiber.
Servings: 2

RECIPE N: 3 - Eggplant Parmesan

Preparation Time: 45 minutes
Ingredients: Eggplant (2, sliced), Marinara sauce (2 cups), Mozzarella cheese (1 cup, shredded), Parmesan cheese (1/2 cup, grated), Breadcrumbs (1 cup), Eggs (2, beaten), Olive oil (for frying), Salt and pepper (to taste)
Method of Cooking: Baking and Frying

Procedure: Dip eggplant slices in egg, then breadcrumbs, fry until golden, layer in baking dish with marinara, mozzarella, parmesan, bake at 375°F until bubbly.
Nutritional Values: High in calcium and fiber.
Servings: 4

RECIPE N: 4 - Vegetarian Chili

Preparation Time: 40 minutes
Ingredients: Kidney beans (1 can, drained), Black beans (1 can, drained), Diced tomatoes (1 can), Onion (1, diced), Bell pepper (1, diced), Garlic (2 cloves, minced), Chili powder (1 tbsp), Cumin (1 tsp), Olive oil (1 tbsp), Salt and pepper (to taste)

Method of Cooking: Simmering
Procedure: Sauté onion, bell pepper, garlic in olive oil, add beans, tomatoes, chili powder, cumin, simmer for 30 minutes, season with salt and pepper.
Nutritional Values: Rich in protein and fiber.
Servings: 4

RECIPE N: 5 - Spinach and Ricotta Stuffed Shells

Preparation Time: 50 minutes
Ingredients: Jumbo pasta shells (20), Ricotta cheese (2 cups), Spinach (2 cups, chopped), Egg (1), Marinara sauce (2 cups), Mozzarella cheese (1 cup, shredded), Parmesan cheese (1/2 cup, grated), Salt and pepper (to taste)
Method of Cooking: Baking

Procedure: Cook shells, mix ricotta, spinach, egg, salt, pepper, stuff into shells, place in baking dish, cover with marinara, mozzarella, parmesan, bake at 375°F until golden.
Nutritional Values: High in calcium and iron.
Servings: 5

RECIPE N: 6 - Thai Tofu Stir-Fry

Preparation Time: 25 minutes
Ingredients: Firm tofu (1 block, cubed), Bell peppers (2, sliced), Carrot (1, julienned), Broccoli (1 cup, florets), Soy sauce (2 tbsp), Peanut butter (1 tbsp), Ginger (1 tsp, grated), Garlic (1 clove, minced), Olive oil (2 tbsp), Lime juice (1 tbsp)
Method of Cooking: Stir-frying

Procedure: Sauté tofu in olive oil until golden, add vegetables, stir-fry, mix soy sauce, peanut butter, ginger, garlic, lime juice for sauce, toss with tofu and veggies.
Nutritional Values: Rich in protein and vitamins.
Servings: 4

RECIPE N: 7 - Caprese Stuffed Portobello Caps

Preparation Time: 20 minutes
Ingredients: Portobello mushroom caps (4), Tomato slices (8), Fresh mozzarella slices (8), Basil leaves (1/2 cup), Balsamic glaze (2 tbsp), Olive oil (1 tbsp), Salt and pepper (to taste)
Method of Cooking: Baking

Procedure: Place tomato, mozzarella, basil inside mushroom caps, drizzle with olive oil, balsamic glaze, season with salt and pepper, bake at 375°F until cheese melts.
Nutritional Values: High in calcium and antioxidants.
Servings: 4

RECIPE N: 8 - Zucchini and Corn Quesadillas

Preparation Time: 20 minutes
Ingredients: Flour tortillas (4), Zucchini (1, thinly sliced), Corn kernels (1 cup), Cheddar cheese (1 cup, shredded), Black beans (1/2 cup, rinsed), Cilantro (1/4 cup, chopped), Olive oil (for cooking), Salt and pepper (to taste)
Method of Cooking: Sautéing and Grilling

Procedure: Sauté zucchini and corn in olive oil, season with salt and pepper, fill tortillas with veggie mix, black beans, cheese, grill until crispy and cheese melts.
Nutritional Values: High in fiber and vitamins.
Servings: 4

RECIPE N: 9 - Creamy Mushroom Risotto

Preparation Time: 45 minutes
Ingredients: Arborio rice (1 cup), Mushrooms (2 cups, sliced), Vegetable broth (4 cups), Onion (1, diced), Garlic (2 cloves, minced), White wine (1/2 cup), Parmesan cheese (1/2 cup, grated), Olive oil (2 tbsp), Salt and pepper (to taste)

Method of Cooking: Simmering
Procedure: Sauté mushrooms, onion, garlic in olive oil, add rice, toast lightly, deglaze with wine, gradually add broth, stir until creamy, finish with parmesan, salt, pepper.
Nutritional Values: Rich in complex carbs and umami flavors.
Servings: 4

RECIPE N: 10 - Baked Falafel with Tzatziki Sauce

Preparation Time: 40 minutes
Ingredients: Chickpeas (2 cups, soaked and drained), Onion (1/2, chopped), Garlic (2 cloves), Parsley (1/4 cup), Cumin (1 tsp), Coriander (1 tsp), Olive oil (for brushing), Greek yogurt (1 cup), Cucumber (1/2, grated), Lemon juice (1 tbsp)
Method of Cooking: Baking

Procedure: Process chickpeas, onion, garlic, parsley, cumin, coriander into a coarse mixture, form into balls, bake at 375°F until crisp; mix yogurt, cucumber, lemon for sauce.
Nutritional Values: High in protein and fiber.
Servings: 4

Stir-Fries and Skillet Meals

RECIPE N: 1 - Chicken and Broccoli Stir-Fry

Preparation Time: 20 minutes

Ingredients: Chicken breast (1 lb, thinly sliced), Broccoli florets (2 cups), Soy sauce (3 tbsp), Honey (1 tbsp), Garlic (2 cloves, minced), Ginger (1 tsp, grated), Sesame oil (1 tbsp), Cornstarch (1 tsp), Olive oil (for stir-frying), Salt and pepper (to taste)

Method of Cooking: Stir-frying

Procedure: Marinate chicken in a mixture of soy sauce, honey, garlic, ginger, cornstarch, and sesame oil; stir-fry in olive oil with broccoli until chicken is cooked through.

Nutritional Values: High in lean protein and vitamin C.

Servings: 4

RECIPE N: 2 - Shrimp and Asparagus Skillet

Preparation Time: 15 minutes

Ingredients: Shrimp (1 lb, peeled), Asparagus (1 bunch, trimmed), Garlic (3 cloves, minced), Lemon zest (1 tsp), Olive oil (2 tbsp), Crushed red pepper flakes (1/2 tsp), Salt and pepper (to taste)

Method of Cooking: Sautéing

Procedure: Sauté asparagus in olive oil until tender-crisp, add shrimp, garlic, lemon zest, red pepper flakes, cook until shrimp are pink and opaque.

Nutritional Values: Rich in protein and essential nutrients.

Servings: 4

RECIPE N: 3 - Beef and Bell Pepper Stir-Fry

Preparation Time: 25 minutes

Ingredients: Beef strips (1 lb), Bell peppers (2, sliced), Soy sauce (2 tbsp), Brown sugar (1 tbsp), Garlic (2 cloves, minced), Olive oil (2 tbsp), Cornstarch (1 tsp), Ginger (1 tsp, grated)

Method of Cooking: Stir-frying

Procedure: Toss beef with cornstarch, soy sauce, brown sugar, ginger, garlic; stir-fry in olive oil with bell peppers until beef is cooked and peppers are tender.

Nutritional Values: High in protein and vitamin A.

Servings: 4

RECIPE N: 4 - Spicy Tofu and Vegetable Skillet

Preparation Time: 20 minutes

Ingredients: Firm tofu (1 block, cubed), Mixed vegetables (carrots, bell peppers, broccoli, 3 cups), Soy sauce (2 tbsp), Sriracha sauce (1 tbsp), Garlic (2 cloves, minced), Sesame oil (1 tbsp), Olive oil (for cooking), Cornstarch (1 tsp)

Method of Cooking: Stir-frying

Procedure: Coat tofu in cornstarch, stir-fry in olive oil until crispy, add vegetables, garlic, stir in soy sauce, sriracha, sesame oil, cook until veggies are tender.

Nutritional Values: Rich in protein and antioxidants.

Servings: 4

RECIPE N: 5 - Lemon Garlic Chicken Skillet

Preparation Time: 25 minutes

Ingredients: Chicken thighs (1.5 lbs, boneless), Garlic (3 cloves, minced), Lemon juice (2 tbsp), Olive oil (2 tbsp), Chicken broth (1/2 cup), Paprika (1 tsp), Salt and pepper (to taste)

Method of Cooking: Sautéing

Procedure: Sauté chicken in olive oil, seasoned with salt, pepper, paprika, add garlic, lemon juice, broth, simmer until chicken is cooked and sauce thickens.

Nutritional Values: High in protein and rich in flavor.

Servings: 4

RECIPE N: 6 - Teriyaki Salmon Stir-Fry

Preparation Time: 20 minutes

Ingredients: Salmon fillets (4, 4 oz each), Teriyaki sauce (1/2 cup), Mixed stir-fry vegetables (4 cups), Garlic (1 clove, minced), Ginger (1 tsp, grated), Sesame seeds (1 tsp), Olive oil (2 tbsp), Salt and pepper (to taste)

Method of Cooking: Stir-frying

Procedure: Sauté salmon fillets in olive oil, season with salt, pepper, remove; stir-fry vegetables with garlic, ginger; return salmon, add teriyaki sauce, garnish with sesame seeds.

Nutritional Values: Rich in omega-3 fatty acids and vitamins.

Servings: 4

RECIPE N: 7 - Spicy Sausage and Kale Skillet

Preparation Time: 30 minutes

Ingredients: Spicy Italian sausage (1 lb, sliced), Kale (2 cups, chopped), Cannellini beans (1 can, drained), Garlic (2 cloves, minced), Chicken broth (1/2 cup), Red pepper flakes (1/2 tsp), Olive oil (1 tbsp), Salt and pepper (to taste)

Method of Cooking: Sautéing

Procedure: Sauté sausage in olive oil until browned, add garlic, kale, beans, broth, red pepper flakes, cook until kale is wilted and sausage is cooked through.

Nutritional Values: High in protein and dietary fiber.

Servings: 4

RECIPE N: 8 - Mushroom and Spinach Frittata

Preparation Time: 25 minutes

Ingredients: Eggs (6, beaten), Mushrooms (1 cup, sliced), Spinach (2 cups), Onion (1, diced), Parmesan cheese (1/4 cup, grated), Olive oil (1 tbsp), Salt and pepper (to taste)

Method of Cooking: Baking and Sautéing

Procedure: Sauté onion, mushrooms in olive oil, add spinach until wilted, pour eggs, sprinkle parmesan, bake at 375°F until eggs are set.

Nutritional Values: Rich in protein and vitamins A and D.

Servings: 4

RECIPE N: 9 - Cauliflower and Chickpea Curry Skillet

Preparation Time: 30 minutes

Ingredients: Cauliflower (1 head, cut into florets), Chickpeas (1 can, drained), Coconut milk (1 can), Curry powder (2 tbsp), Garlic (1 clove, minced), Onion (1, diced), Olive oil (1 tbsp), Salt and pepper (to taste)

Method of Cooking: Sautéing and Simmering

Procedure: Sauté onion, garlic in olive oil, add cauliflower, chickpeas, curry powder, coconut milk, simmer until cauliflower is tender and flavors meld.

Nutritional Values: High in fiber and plant-based protein.

Servings: 4

RECIPE N: 10 - Skillet Lasagna

Preparation Time: 40 minutes

Ingredients: Ground beef (1 lb), Lasagna noodles (8, broken), Marinara sauce (2 cups), Ricotta cheese (1 cup), Mozzarella cheese (1 cup, shredded), Parmesan cheese (1/2 cup, grated), Garlic (1 clove, minced), Olive oil (1 tbsp), Salt and pepper (to taste)

Method of Cooking: Sautéing and Simmering.

Procedure: Brown beef in olive oil, add garlic, marinara, water, noodles, simmer until noodles are cooked, dollop with ricotta, sprinkle mozzarella, parmesan, cover until cheese melts.

Nutritional Values: Rich in protein and calcium.

Servings: 4

Chapter 7: Snacks and Small Bites

Healthy Snack Options

RECIPE N: 1 - Apple Cinnamon Yogurt Bowl

Preparation Time: 10 minutes
Ingredients: Greek yogurt (1 cup), Apple (1, diced), Cinnamon (1/2 tsp), Honey (1 tbsp), Almonds (1/4 cup, sliced)
Method of Cooking: No cooking required

Procedure: Mix Greek yogurt with diced apple, a sprinkle of cinnamon, drizzle with honey, top with sliced almonds.
Nutritional Values: Rich in protein and fiber.
Servings:1

RECIPE N: 2 - Veggie Sticks with Hummus

Preparation Time: 10 minutes

Ingredients: Carrot (1, julienned), Cucumber (1, julienned), Bell pepper (1, sliced), Hummus (1/2 cup)

Method of Cooking: No cooking required

Procedure: Serve julienned carrot, cucumber, and sliced bell pepper with a side of hummus for dipping.

Nutritional Values: High in vitamins and dietary fiber.

Servings: 2

RECIPE N: 3 - Baked Kale Chips

Preparation Time: 15 minutes

Ingredients: Kale leaves (2 cups, torn), Olive oil (1 tbsp), Sea salt (1/2 tsp), Garlic powder (1/2 tsp)

Method of Cooking: Baking

Procedure: Toss kale leaves with olive oil, sea salt, garlic powder, bake at 350°F until crispy.

Nutritional Values: Low in calories, high in vitamins.

Servings: 2

RECIPE N: 4 - Peanut Butter Banana Bites

Preparation Time: 10 minutes

Ingredients: Banana (1, sliced), Peanut butter (1/4 cup), Dark chocolate chips (1/4 cup), Granola (1/4 cup)

Method of Cooking: No cooking required

Procedure: Spread peanut butter on banana slices, sprinkle with dark chocolate chips and granola.

Nutritional Values: Good source of potassium and healthy fats.

Servings: 2

RECIPE N: 5 - Avocado Toast with Cherry Tomatoes

Preparation Time: 5 minutes

Ingredients: Whole grain bread (2 slices, toasted), Avocado (1, mashed), Cherry tomatoes (1/2 cup, halved), Salt and pepper (to taste)

Method of Cooking: Toasting

Procedure: Spread mashed avocado on toasted bread, top with halved cherry tomatoes, season with salt and pepper.

Nutritional Values: Rich in healthy fats and fiber.

Servings: 2

RECIPE N: 6 - Spiced Roasted Chickpeas

Preparation Time: 30 minutes

Ingredients: Chickpeas (1 can, drained), Olive oil (1 tbsp), Paprika (1 tsp), Cumin (1/2 tsp), Garlic powder (1/2 tsp), Salt (to taste)

Method of Cooking: Roasting

Procedure: Toss chickpeas with olive oil, paprika, cumin, garlic powder, salt, roast at 400°F until crispy.

Nutritional Values: High in protein and fiber.

Servings: 2

RECIPE N: 7 - Greek Yogurt and Mixed Berries

Preparation Time: 5 minutes

Ingredients: Greek yogurt (1 cup), Mixed berries (1/2 cup), Honey (1 tbsp), Chia seeds (1 tsp)

Method of Cooking: No cooking required

Procedure: Combine Greek yogurt with mixed berries, drizzle with honey, sprinkle chia seeds.

Nutritional Values: Rich in antioxidants and probiotics.

Servings: 1

RECIPE N: 8 - Cucumber and Cream Cheese Bites

Preparation Time: 10 minutes

Ingredients: Cucumber (1, sliced), Cream cheese (1/4 cup), Dill (1 tsp, chopped), Salt and pepper (to taste)

Method of Cooking: No cooking required

Procedure: Top cucumber slices with cream cheese, sprinkle with dill, season with salt and pepper.

Nutritional Values: Low in calories, refreshing.

Servings: 2

RECIPE N: 9 - Almond and Date Energy Balls

Preparation Time: 20 minutes

Ingredients: Dates (1 cup, pitted), Almonds (1/2 cup), Coconut flakes (1/4 cup), Cocoa powder (1 tbsp), Sea salt (a pinch)

Method of Cooking: Blending

Procedure: Blend dates, almonds, coconut flakes, cocoa powder, sea salt until sticky, form into balls.

Nutritional Values: Rich in natural sugars and healthy fats.

Servings: 4

RECIPE N: 10 - Caprese Skewers

Preparation Time: 10 minutes

Ingredients: Cherry tomatoes (1 cup), Mini mozzarella balls (1 cup), Basil leaves (20), Balsamic glaze (2 tbsp), Olive oil (1 tbsp)

Method of Cooking: No cooking required

Procedure: Skewer cherry tomatoes, mozzarella, basil leaves, drizzle with balsamic glaze and olive oil.

Nutritional Values: High in calcium and vitamins.

Servings: 4

Dips and Spreads

RECIPE N: 1 - Roasted Red Pepper Hummus

Preparation Time: 15 minutes

Ingredients: Chickpeas (1 can, drained), Roasted red peppers (1/2 cup), Tahini (2 tbsp), Lemon juice (1 tbsp), Garlic (1 clove), Olive oil (2 tbsp), Cumin (1/2 tsp), Salt (to taste)

Method of Cooking: Blending

Procedure: Blend chickpeas, roasted red peppers, tahini, lemon juice, garlic, olive oil, cumin, and salt until smooth.

Nutritional Values: Rich in protein and healthy fats.

Servings: 4

RECIPE N: 2 - Greek Tzatziki Dip

Preparation Time: 10 minutes

Ingredients: Greek yogurt (1 cup), Cucumber (1, grated and drained), Garlic (1 clove, minced), Dill (1 tbsp, chopped), Lemon juice (1 tbsp), Olive oil (1 tsp), Salt and pepper (to taste)

Method of Cooking: Mixing

Procedure: Combine Greek yogurt, grated cucumber, minced garlic, dill, lemon juice, olive oil, season with salt and pepper.

Nutritional Values: High in calcium and probiotics.

Servings: 4

RECIPE N: 3 - Avocado and Cilantro Dip

Preparation Time: 10 minutes

Ingredients: Avocado (2, ripe), Cilantro (1/4 cup, chopped), Lime juice (2 tbsp), Garlic (1 clove, minced), Jalapeño (1, seeded and minced), Salt (to taste)

Method of Cooking: Mashing

Procedure: Mash ripe avocados, mix in chopped cilantro, lime juice, minced garlic, jalapeño, season with salt.

Nutritional Values: Rich in healthy fats and vitamins.

Servings: 4

RECIPE N: 4 - Sun-Dried Tomato Pesto

Preparation Time: 10 minutes

Ingredients: Sun-dried tomatoes (1/2 cup), Basil leaves (1/4 cup), Pine nuts (2 tbsp), Garlic (1 clove), Olive oil (1/4 cup), Parmesan cheese (2 tbsp, grated), Salt (to taste)

Method of Cooking: Blending

Procedure: Blend sun-dried tomatoes, basil, pine nuts, garlic, olive oil, parmesan cheese, season with salt.

Nutritional Values: High in antioxidants and flavor.

Servings: 4

RECIPE N: 5 - Classic Bean Dip

Preparation Time: 15 minutes

Ingredients: Refried beans (1 can), Cream cheese (1/4 cup), Taco seasoning (1 tbsp), Cheddar cheese (1/2 cup, shredded), Green onions (2 tbsp, chopped)

Method of Cooking: Layering and Baking

Procedure: Layer refried beans, cream cheese mixed with taco seasoning, top with cheddar cheese, bake until bubbly, garnish with green onions.

Nutritional Values: High in protein and fiber.

Servings: 4

RECIPE N: 6 - Spicy Mango Salsa

Preparation Time: 15 minutes

Ingredients: Mango (2, diced), Red onion (1/4 cup, finely chopped), Jalapeño (1, seeded and minced), Cilantro (1/4 cup, chopped), Lime juice (2 tbsp), Salt (to taste)

Method of Cooking: Mixing

Procedure: Combine diced mango, red onion, jalapeño, cilantro, and lime juice, season with salt for a tangy and spicy salsa.

Nutritional Values: Rich in vitamins A and C.

Servings: 4

RECIPE N: 7 - Creamy Spinach Artichoke Dip

Preparation Time: 20 minutes

Ingredients: Spinach (1 cup, chopped), Artichoke hearts (1 cup, chopped), Cream cheese (1/2 cup), Sour cream (1/4 cup), Parmesan cheese (1/4 cup, grated), Garlic (1 clove, minced), Salt and pepper (to taste)

Method of Cooking: Baking
Procedure: Mix together spinach, artichokes, cream cheese, sour cream, parmesan, garlic, season with salt, pepper, bake until bubbly and golden.
Nutritional Values: High in calcium and fiber.
Servings: 4

RECIPE N: 8 - Black Olive Tapenade

Preparation Time: 10 minutes

Ingredients: Black olives (1 cup, pitted), Capers (1 tbsp), Garlic (1 clove), Olive oil (1/4 cup), Lemon juice (1 tbsp), Anchovy paste (1 tsp, optional)
Method of Cooking: Blending

Procedure: Blend black olives, capers, garlic, olive oil, lemon juice, and anchovy paste for a savory Mediterranean spread.
Nutritional Values: Rich in healthy fats and umami flavor.
Servings: 4

RECIPE N: 9 - Roasted Garlic and White Bean Dip

Preparation Time: 40 minutes

Ingredients: Cannellini beans (1 can, drained), Garlic (1 head, roasted), Olive oil (2 tbsp), Lemon juice (1 tbsp), Rosemary (1 tsp, chopped), Salt and pepper (to taste)
Method of Cooking: Blending

Procedure: Blend roasted garlic, cannellini beans, olive oil, lemon juice, rosemary, season with salt and pepper for a creamy dip.
Nutritional Values: High in protein and fiber.
Servings: 4

RECIPE N: 10 - Fiery Sichuan Eggplant Dip

Preparation Time: 25 minutes

Ingredients: Eggplant (2, roasted and peeled), Tahini (2 tbsp), Soy sauce (1 tbsp), Sichuan chili oil (1 tbsp), Garlic (1 clove, minced), Green onion (1, chopped), Sesame seeds (1 tsp)

Method of Cooking: Blending
Procedure: Blend roasted eggplant, tahini, soy sauce, chili oil, garlic, garnish with green onion, sesame seeds for a spicy Asian-inspired dip.
Nutritional Values: Rich in antioxidants and spicy flavors.
Servings: 4

Homemade Energy Bars and Bites

RECIPE N: 1 - Almond Coconut Energy Bars

Preparation Time: 15 minutes + Chilling

Ingredients: Almonds (1 cup, chopped), Dates (1 cup, pitted), Shredded coconut (1/2 cup), Chia seeds (2 tbsp), Coconut oil (2 tbsp), Honey (2 tbsp), Vanilla extract (1 tsp)

Method of Cooking: No cooking required

Procedure: Process almonds, dates, coconut, chia seeds, coconut oil, honey, vanilla in a food processor, press into a pan, chill until set, cut into bars.

Nutritional Values: High in healthy fats and protein.

Servings: 8

RECIPE N: 2 - Peanut Butter Chocolate Chip Bites

Preparation Time: 10 minutes + Chilling

Ingredients: Oats (1 cup), Peanut butter (1/2 cup), Honey (1/4 cup), Dark chocolate chips (1/4 cup), Flaxseeds (2 tbsp), Vanilla extract (1 tsp)

Method of Cooking: No cooking required

Procedure: Mix oats, peanut butter, honey, chocolate chips, flaxseeds, vanilla, form into small balls, chill in the fridge until firm.

Nutritional Values: Rich in fiber and antioxidants.

Servings: 10

RECIPE N: 3 - Cranberry Pistachio Energy Squares

Preparation Time: 20 minutes + Freezing

Ingredients: Dried cranberries (1/2 cup), Pistachios (1/2 cup, shelled), Rolled oats (1 cup), Sunflower seeds (1/4 cup), Honey (1/3 cup), Coconut oil (1/4 cup), Vanilla extract (1 tsp)

Method of Cooking: No cooking required

Procedure: Combine cranberries, pistachios, oats, sunflower seeds, honey, coconut oil, vanilla, press into a pan, freeze until solid, cut into squares.

Nutritional Values: A good source of energy and nutrients.

Servings: 8

Chapter 8: Comforting Soups and Stews

Warm and Nourishing Soups

RECIPE N: 1 - Rustic Vegetable Minestrone

Preparation Time: 40 minutes

Ingredients: Olive oil (2 tbsp), Onion (1, chopped), Carrots (2, diced), Celery (2 stalks, diced), Garlic (2 cloves, minced), Canned tomatoes (1 can, crushed), Vegetable broth (4 cups), Kidney beans (1 can, drained), Zucchini (1, diced), Pasta (1 cup, small shape), Basil (1 tbsp, chopped), Salt and pepper (to taste)

Method of Cooking: Simmering

Procedure: Sauté onion, carrots, celery, garlic in olive oil, add tomatoes, broth, beans, simmer, add zucchini, pasta, cook until tender, season with basil, salt, pepper.

Nutritional Values: High in fiber and vitamins.

Servings: 4

RECIPE N: 2 - Creamy Butternut Squash Soup

Preparation Time: 45 minutes

Ingredients: Butternut squash (1, peeled and cubed), Onion (1, diced), Garlic (2 cloves), Vegetable broth (4 cups), Coconut milk (1 cup), Nutmeg (1/2 tsp), Olive oil (2 tbsp), Salt and pepper (to taste)

Method of Cooking: Blending

Procedure: Roast squash with onion, garlic, olive oil, blend with broth, coconut milk, nutmeg, heat until warm, season with salt, pepper.

Nutritional Values: Rich in vitamins A and C.

Servings: 4

RECIPE N: 3 - Classic Chicken Noodle Soup

Preparation Time: 1 hour

Ingredients: Chicken breasts (2, bone-in), Carrots (2, diced), Celery (2 stalks, diced), Onion (1, diced), Egg noodles (1 cup), Chicken broth (6 cups), Thyme (1 tsp), Salt and pepper (to taste)

Method of Cooking: Boiling and Simmering

Procedure: Boil chicken, remove, shred meat; in same pot, add carrots, celery, onion, broth, noodles, thyme, chicken, simmer until vegetables are tender.

Nutritional Values: High in protein.

Servings: 4

RECIPE N: 4 - Lentil and Sweet Potato Stew

Preparation Time: 50 minutes

Ingredients: Lentils (1 cup), Sweet potatoes (2, cubed), Onion (1, diced), Vegetable broth (4 cups), Spinach (2 cups), Cumin (1 tsp), Olive oil (2 tbsp), Salt and pepper (to taste)

Method of Cooking: Simmering

Procedure: Sauté onion in olive oil, add sweet potatoes, lentils, broth, cumin, simmer until lentils are tender, stir in spinach, season with salt, pepper.

Nutritional Values: Rich in fiber and plant-based protein.

Servings: 4

Hearty Stews

RECIPE N: 1 - Beef and Barley Stew

Preparation Time: 1 hour 30 minutes

Ingredients: Beef chunks (1 lb), Barley (1/2 cup), Carrots (2, chopped), Celery (2 stalks, chopped), Onion (1, chopped), Beef broth (4 cups), Tomato paste (2 tbsp), Thyme (1 tsp), Olive oil (2 tbsp), Salt and pepper (to taste)

Method of Cooking: Simmering

Procedure: Brown beef in olive oil, add vegetables, barley, broth, tomato paste, thyme, simmer until beef is tender and barley cooked.

Nutritional Values: High in protein and fiber.

Servings: 4

RECIPE N: 2 - Hearty Chicken and Vegetable Stew

Preparation Time: 1 hour

Ingredients: Chicken thighs (1 lb, boneless), Potatoes (2, diced), Carrots (2, chopped), Peas (1 cup), Chicken broth (4 cups), Onion (1, chopped), Garlic (2 cloves, minced), Olive oil (2 tbsp), Rosemary (1 tsp), Salt and pepper (to taste)

Method of Cooking: Simmering

Procedure: Sauté chicken, onion, garlic in olive oil, add potatoes, carrots, peas, broth, rosemary, simmer until chicken is cooked and vegetables tender.

Nutritional Values: Rich in vitamins and minerals.

Servings: 4

RECIPE N: 3 - Moroccan Lentil and Chickpea Stew

Preparation Time: 45 minutes

Ingredients: Lentils (1 cup), Chickpeas (1 can, drained), Canned tomatoes (1 can, crushed), Onion (1, diced), Carrots (2, diced), Vegetable broth (4 cups), Cumin (1 tsp), Cinnamon (1/2 tsp), Coriander (1 tsp), Olive oil (2 tbsp), Salt and pepper (to taste)
4

Method of Cooking: Simmering

Procedure: Sauté onion, carrots in olive oil, add lentils, chickpeas, tomatoes, broth, cumin, cinnamon, coriander, simmer until lentils are tender.

Nutritional Values: High in plant-based protein and fiber.

Servings:

Light and Brothy Options

RECIPE N: 1 - Ginger Miso Soup

Preparation Time: 20 minutes
Ingredients: Miso paste (2 tbsp), Vegetable broth (4 cups), Tofu (1/2 cup, cubed), Carrots (1/2 cup, thinly sliced), Ginger (1 inch, grated), Green onions (2, chopped), Seaweed (1/4 cup, dried)
Method of Cooking: Simmering

Procedure: Dissolve miso paste in warm broth, add tofu, carrots, ginger, simmer gently, garnish with green onions and seaweed.
Nutritional Values: Rich in probiotics and vitamins.
Servings: 4

RECIPE N: 2 - Lemon Chicken Orzo Soup

Preparation Time: 30 minutes

Ingredients: Chicken breast (1, shredded), Orzo pasta (1/2 cup), Chicken broth (4 cups), Lemon juice (2 tbsp), Carrots (1/2 cup, diced), Celery (1/2 cup, diced), Dill (1 tbsp, chopped), Olive oil (1 tbsp), Salt and pepper (to taste)

Method of Cooking: Boiling
Procedure: Sauté carrots, celery in olive oil, add broth, orzo, cook until pasta is tender, add chicken, lemon juice, dill, season with salt, pepper.
Nutritional Values: High in protein and vitamin C.
Servings: 4

RECIPE N: 3 - Tomato Basil Broth

Preparation Time: 25 minutes

Ingredients: Canned tomatoes (1 can, crushed), Vegetable broth (4 cups), Fresh basil (1/4 cup, chopped), Garlic (2 cloves, minced), Onion (1, diced), Olive oil (1 tbsp), Salt and pepper (to taste)
Method of Cooking: Simmering

Procedure: Sauté onion, garlic in olive oil, add tomatoes, broth, simmer, blend until smooth, add basil, season with salt, pepper.
Nutritional Values: Low in calories, high in lycopene.
Servings: 4

Chapter 9: Side Dishes and Salads

Vegetable Sides

RECIPE N: 1 - Garlic Roasted Brussels Sprouts

Preparation Time: 25 minutes

Ingredients: Brussels sprouts (1 lb, halved), Garlic (3 cloves, minced), Olive oil (2 tbsp), Lemon juice (1 tbsp), Parmesan cheese (2 tbsp, grated), Salt and pepper (to taste)
Method of Cooking: Roasting

Procedure: Toss Brussels sprouts with garlic, olive oil, roast at 400°F until caramelized, drizzle with lemon juice, sprinkle with Parmesan, season with salt, pepper.
Nutritional Values: High in vitamins C and K.
Servings: 4

RECIPE N: 2 - Balsamic Glazed Carrots

Preparation Time: 30 minutes

Ingredients: Carrots (1 lb, sliced), Balsamic vinegar (2 tbsp), Honey (1 tbsp), Olive oil (2 tbsp), Thyme (1 tsp), Salt and pepper (to taste)

Method of Cooking: Roasting

Procedure: Roast carrots with olive oil, salt, pepper, until tender, glaze with balsamic vinegar and honey, garnish with thyme.

Nutritional Values: Rich in beta-carotene and antioxidants.

Servings: 4

RECIPE N: 3 - Spiced Cauliflower Steaks

Preparation Time: 30 minutes

Ingredients: Cauliflower (1 head, sliced into steaks), Cumin (1 tsp), Paprika (1 tsp), Olive oil (3 tbsp), Lemon juice (2 tbsp), Salt and pepper (to taste)

Method of Cooking: Grilling

Procedure: Brush cauliflower steaks with olive oil, season with cumin, paprika, salt, pepper, grill until charred, drizzle with lemon juice.

Nutritional Values: Low in calories, high in fiber.

Servings: 4

RECIPE N: 4 - Sautéed Green Beans with Almonds

Preparation Time: 20 minutes

Ingredients: Green beans (1 lb, trimmed), Sliced almonds (1/4 cup), Garlic (2 cloves, minced), Olive oil (2 tbsp), Lemon zest (1 tsp), Salt and pepper (to taste)

Method of Cooking: Sautéing

Procedure: Sauté green beans, garlic in olive oil until tender-crisp, add almonds, cook until golden, garnish with lemon zest, season with salt, pepper.

Nutritional Values: Good source of vitamins A, C, and K.

Servings: 4

Grain and Legume-Based Dishes

RECIPE N: 1 - Quinoa Tabbouleh

Preparation Time: 25 minutes

Ingredients: Quinoa (1 cup, cooked), Cucumber (1, diced), Tomatoes (2, diced), Parsley (1 cup, chopped), Lemon juice (3 tbsp), Olive oil (2 tbsp), Mint (1/4 cup, chopped), Salt and pepper (to taste)
Method of Cooking: Mixing

Procedure: Combine cooked quinoa, cucumber, tomatoes, parsley, mint, dress with lemon juice, olive oil, season with salt, pepper.
Nutritional Values: High in protein and fiber.
Servings: 4

RECIPE N: 2 - Lentil and Roasted Sweet Potato Salad

Preparation Time: 40 minutes

Ingredients: Lentils (1 cup, cooked), Sweet potatoes (2, cubed and roasted), Arugula (2 cups), Red onion (1/4 cup, thinly sliced), Feta cheese (1/4 cup, crumbled), Balsamic vinaigrette (3 tbsp), Salt and pepper (to taste)

Method of Cooking: Roasting and Mixing
Procedure: Toss roasted sweet potatoes, cooked lentils, arugula, red onion, feta, drizzle with balsamic vinaigrette, season with salt, pepper.
Nutritional Values: Rich in vitamins, minerals, and plant-based protein.
Servings: 4

RECIPE N: 3 - Mediterranean Farro Salad

Preparation Time: 30 minutes

Ingredients: Farro (1 cup, cooked), Cherry tomatoes (1 cup, halved), Cucumber (1, diced), Kalamata olives (1/4 cup, pitted), Feta cheese (1/4 cup, crumbled), Lemon vinaigrette (3 tbsp), Parsley (1/4 cup, chopped), Salt and pepper (to taste)

Method of Cooking: Mixing
Procedure: Combine farro, cherry tomatoes, cucumber, olives, feta, parsley, dress with lemon vinaigrette, season with salt, pepper.
Nutritional Values: High in fiber and healthy fats.
Servings: 4

RECIPE N: 4 - Chickpea and Avocado Salad

Preparation Time: 15 minutes

Ingredients: Chickpeas (1 can, drained), Avocado (1, cubed), Red bell pepper (1, diced), Red onion (1/4 cup, finely chopped), Cilantro (1/4 cup, chopped), Lime juice (2 tbsp), Olive oil (1 tbsp), Salt and pepper (to taste)

Method of Cooking: Mixing

Procedure: Mix chickpeas, avocado, bell pepper, red onion, cilantro, dress with lime juice, olive oil, season with salt, pepper.

Nutritional Values: Rich in protein and healthy fats.

Servings: 4

Creative Salad Combinations

RECIPE N: 1 - Asian Pear and Arugula Salad

Preparation Time: 15 minutes

Ingredients: Arugula (2 cups), Asian pear (1, thinly sliced), Walnuts (1/4 cup, toasted), Gorgonzola cheese (1/4 cup, crumbled), Balsamic vinaigrette (2 tbsp), Honey (1 tsp), Salt and pepper (to taste)

Method of Cooking: Mixing

Procedure: Toss arugula, Asian pear slices, toasted walnuts, and Gorgonzola cheese, dress with balsamic vinaigrette mixed with honey, season with salt, pepper.

Nutritional Values: Rich in vitamins, minerals, and antioxidants.

Servings: 2

RECIPE N: 2 - Roasted Beet and Goat Cheese Salad

Preparation Time: 45 minutes

Ingredients: Beets (3, roasted and sliced), Goat cheese (1/4 cup, crumbled), Mixed greens (2 cups), Walnuts (1/4 cup, toasted), Orange vinaigrette (2 tbsp), Orange zest (1 tsp), Salt and pepper (to taste)

Method of Cooking: Roasting and Mixing

Procedure: Combine roasted beet slices, mixed greens, crumbled goat cheese, and toasted walnuts, dress with orange vinaigrette, garnish with orange zest.

Nutritional Values: High in fiber and vitamin C.

Servings: 2

RECIPE N: 3 - Avocado and Grapefruit Salad

Preparation Time: 20 minutes

Ingredients: Avocado (1, sliced), Grapefruit (1, segments), Mixed greens (2 cups), Red onion (1/4 cup, thinly sliced), Citrus vinaigrette (2 tbsp), Pumpkin seeds (2 tbsp), Salt and pepper (to taste)

Method of Cooking: Mixing

Procedure: Arrange avocado slices, grapefruit segments on a bed of mixed greens, sprinkle with red onion, pumpkin seeds, drizzle with citrus vinaigrette.

Nutritional Values: Rich in healthy fats and vitamin E.

Servings: 2

RECIPE N: 4 - Watermelon and Feta Salad

Preparation Time: 15 minutes

Ingredients: Watermelon (2 cups, cubed), Feta cheese (1/2 cup, crumbled), Mint leaves (1/4 cup, chopped), Black olives (1/4 cup, sliced), Lime vinaigrette (2 tbsp), Salt and pepper (to taste)

Method of Cooking: Mixing

Procedure: Toss watermelon cubes with crumbled feta cheese, chopped mint leaves, and sliced black olives, dress with lime vinaigrette, season with salt, pepper.

Nutritional Values: High in hydration and calcium.

Servings: 4

Chapter 10: Desserts and Sweet Treats

Fruit-Based Desserts

RECIPE N: 1 - Baked Cinnamon Apples

Preparation Time: 30 minutes

Ingredients: Apples (4, cored and sliced), Cinnamon (1 tsp), Nutmeg (1/4 tsp), Honey (2 tbsp), Lemon juice (1 tbsp), Water (1/4 cup)
Method of Cooking: Baking

4

Procedure: Arrange apple slices in a baking dish, sprinkle with cinnamon, nutmeg, drizzle with honey, lemon juice, add water, bake until tender.
Nutritional Values: High in fiber and natural sweetness.
Servings:

RECIPE N: 2 - Mango Coconut Chia Pudding

Preparation Time: 4 hours (including chilling)

Ingredients: Chia seeds (1/4 cup), Coconut milk (1 cup), Mango (1, pureed), Honey (1 tbsp), Shredded coconut (2 tbsp), Lime zest (1 tsp)

Method of Cooking: Refrigerating

Procedure: Mix chia seeds with coconut milk, let sit until thickened, layer with mango puree, top with shredded coconut, lime zest, chill.

Nutritional Values: Rich in omega-3 fatty acids and vitamins.

Servings: 2

RECIPE N: 3 - Grilled Peaches with Yogurt

Preparation Time: 20 minutes

Ingredients: Peaches (4, halved and pitted), Greek yogurt (1 cup), Honey (2 tbsp), Cinnamon (1/2 tsp), Mint leaves (for garnish)

Method of Cooking: Grilling

Procedure: Grill peach halves until caramelized, serve with a dollop of Greek yogurt, drizzle with honey, sprinkle with cinnamon, garnish with mint.

Nutritional Values: High in calcium and antioxidants.

Servings: 4

RECIPE N: 4 - Berry Fruit Salad with Honey Lime Dressing

Preparation Time: 15 minutes

Ingredients: Mixed berries (2 cups), Honey (2 tbsp), Lime juice (1 tbsp), Mint leaves (1/4 cup, chopped), Lime zest (1 tsp)

Method of Cooking: Mixing

Procedure: Toss mixed berries with honey, lime juice, mint leaves, garnish with lime zest for a refreshing fruit salad.

Nutritional Values: Rich in vitamins and antioxidants.

Servings: 4

Low-Fat Baking Recipes

RECIPE N: 1 - Low-Fat Banana Bread

Preparation Time: 1 hour

Ingredients: Ripe bananas (3, mashed), Whole wheat flour (1 1/2 cups), Baking powder (1 tsp), Baking soda (1/2 tsp), Cinnamon (1 tsp), Honey (1/2 cup), Unsweetened applesauce (1/4 cup), Egg (1), Vanilla extract (1 tsp)

Method of Cooking: Baking

Procedure: Combine mashed bananas, honey, applesauce, egg, vanilla, then mix with flour, baking powder, soda, cinnamon, bake at 350°F.

Nutritional Values: High in potassium and fiber.

Servings: 10

RECIPE N: 2 - Zucchini Chocolate Chip Muffins

Preparation Time: 30 minutes

Ingredients: Grated zucchini (1 cup), Whole wheat flour (1 3/4 cups), Baking soda (1 tsp), Cinnamon (1 tsp), Unsweetened applesauce (1/2 cup), Honey (1/3 cup), Egg (1), Dark chocolate chips (1/4 cup)

Method of Cooking: Baking

Procedure: Mix zucchini, applesauce, honey, egg, then add flour, baking soda, cinnamon, fold in chocolate chips, bake at 375°F.

Nutritional Values: Low in fat, high in moisture and flavor.

Servings: 12 muffins

RECIPE N: 3 - Apple Oatmeal Cookies

Preparation Time: 25 minutes

Ingredients: Rolled oats (1 cup), Whole wheat flour (3/4 cup), Baking powder (1 tsp), Cinnamon (1 tsp), Diced apple (1 cup), Unsweetened applesauce (1/2 cup), Honey (1/4 cup), Egg (1)

Method of Cooking: Baking

Procedure: Combine oats, flour, baking powder, cinnamon, mix in applesauce, honey, egg, fold in apples, drop onto baking sheet, bake at 350°F.

Nutritional Values: Rich in fiber and natural sweetness.

Servings: 15 cookies

RECIPE N: 4 - Carrot Cake Squares

Preparation Time: 35 minutes

Ingredients: Grated carrots (1 cup), Whole wheat flour (1 cup), Baking powder (1 tsp), Cinnamon (1 tsp), Unsweetened applesauce (1/2 cup), Honey (1/3 cup), Egg (1), Walnuts (1/4 cup, chopped)

Method of Cooking: Baking

Procedure: Mix grated carrots, applesauce, honey, egg, then add flour, baking powder, cinnamon, walnuts, pour into pan, bake at 350°F.

Nutritional Values: High in vitamin A and healthy fats.

Servings: 9 squares

Guilt-Free Sweet Snacks

RECIPE N: 1 - Frozen Greek Yogurt Bark

Preparation Time: 4 hours (including freezing)

Ingredients: Greek yogurt (2 cups, plain), Honey (2 tbsp), Mixed berries (1 cup), Sliced almonds (1/4 cup), Unsweetened coconut flakes (1/4 cup)

Method of Cooking: Freezing

Procedure: Spread Greek yogurt on a baking sheet, drizzle with honey, top with mixed berries, almonds, coconut, freeze until solid, break into pieces.

Nutritional Values: High in protein and antioxidants.

Servings: 6

RECIPE N: 2 - Peanut Butter Protein Balls

Preparation Time: 15 minutes + Chilling

Ingredients: Natural peanut butter (1 cup), Oats (1 cup), Honey (1/4 cup), Protein powder (1/2 cup, vanilla or chocolate flavor), Mini dark chocolate chips (1/4 cup)

Method of Cooking: No cooking required

Procedure: Mix peanut butter, oats, honey, protein powder, chocolate chips, form into balls, chill in the refrigerator until firm.

Nutritional Values: Rich in protein and healthy fats.

Servings: 10

RECIPE N: 3 - Cinnamon Apple Chips

Preparation Time: 2 hours 15 minutes

Ingredients: Apples (2, thinly sliced), Cinnamon (1 tsp), Sugar (optional, 1 tbsp)

Method of Cooking: Baking

Procedure: Lay apple slices on a baking sheet, sprinkle with cinnamon, sugar if desired, bake at 200°F until crispy.

Nutritional Values: Low in calories, high in fiber.

Servings: 4

RECIPE N: 4 - No-Bake Oatmeal Date Bars

Preparation Time: 1 hour (including chilling)

Ingredients: Rolled oats (1 cup), Dates (1 cup, pitted), Peanut butter (1/2 cup), Honey (1/4 cup), Chopped nuts (1/2 cup, your choice)

Method of Cooking: No cooking required

Procedure: Process oats, dates, peanut butter, honey in a food processor, stir in nuts, press into a pan, chill, cut into bars.

Nutritional Values: High in fiber and natural sugars.

Servings: 8

Chapter 11: Beverages and Smoothies

Nutritious Smoothies

RECIPE N: 1 - Antioxidant Berry Blast Smoothie

Preparation Time: 5 minutes
Ingredients: Frozen mixed berries (1 cup), Spinach (1 cup), Greek yogurt (1/2 cup), Almond milk (1 cup), Chia seeds (1 tbsp), Honey (1 tbsp)
Method of Cooking: Blending

Procedure: Blend frozen berries, spinach, Greek yogurt, almond milk, chia seeds, and honey until smooth for a nutrient-packed drink.
Nutritional Values: Rich in antioxidants, vitamins, and omega-3 fatty acids.
Servings: 2

RECIPE N: 2 - Tropical Green Smoothie

Preparation Time: 5 minutes

Ingredients: Pineapple chunks (1 cup), Mango (1/2 cup), Spinach (1 cup), Coconut water (1 cup), Banana (1), Flaxseeds (1 tbsp)
Method of Cooking: Blending

Procedure: Combine pineapple, mango, spinach, coconut water, banana, and flaxseeds in a blender, blend until creamy and smooth.
Nutritional Values: High in vitamins A and C, and hydration.
Servings: 2

RECIPE N: 3 - Protein-Packed Peanut Butter Smoothie

Preparation Time: 5 minutes

Ingredients: Banana (1), Natural peanut butter (2 tbsp), Greek yogurt (1/2 cup), Almond milk (1 cup), Protein powder (1 scoop, optional), Cinnamon (1/2 tsp)
Method of Cooking: Blending

Procedure: Blend banana, peanut butter, Greek yogurt, almond milk, protein powder if using, and cinnamon for a satisfying, protein-rich drink.
Nutritional Values: High in protein and potassium.
Servings: 1

RECIPE N: 4 - Blueberry Oatmeal Breakfast Smoothie

Preparation Time: 5 minutes
Ingredients: Blueberries (1 cup, frozen), Rolled oats (1/4 cup), Greek yogurt (1/2 cup), Almond milk (1 cup), Honey (1 tbsp), Vanilla extract (1 tsp)
Method of Cooking: Blending

Procedure: Blend blueberries, oats, Greek yogurt, almond milk, honey, and vanilla extract for a filling and nutritious breakfast smoothie.
Nutritional Values: Rich in fiber and antioxidants.
Servings: 2

Herbal Teas and Infusions

RECIPE N: 1 - Chamomile Lavender Tea

Preparation Time: 10 minutes

Ingredients: Dried chamomile flowers (1 tbsp), Dried lavender buds (1 tsp), Honey (optional, 1 tbsp), Boiling water (1 cup)
Method of Cooking: Steeping

Procedure: Steep chamomile flowers and lavender buds in boiling water for 5 minutes, strain, sweeten with honey if desired.
Nutritional Values: Calming, aids in relaxation and digestion. **Servings**: 1

RECIPE N: 2 - Peppermint and Lemon Balm Tea

Preparation Time: 10 minutes

Ingredients: Fresh peppermint leaves (1/4 cup), Fresh lemon balm leaves (1/4 cup), Honey (optional, 1 tbsp), Boiling water (1 cup)

Method of Cooking: Steeping

Procedure: Steep peppermint and lemon balm leaves in boiling water for 5 minutes, strain, add honey for sweetness if preferred.

Nutritional Values: Refreshing, aids in stress relief and digestion.

Servings: 1

RECIPE N: 3 - Ginger Turmeric Infusion

Preparation Time: 15 minutes

Ingredients: Fresh ginger root (1 inch, sliced), Turmeric powder (1/2 tsp), Lemon juice (1 tbsp), Honey (1 tbsp), Hot water (1 cup)

Method of Cooking: Infusing

Procedure: Infuse sliced ginger, turmeric powder in hot water for 10 minutes, add lemon juice, honey, strain before serving.

Nutritional Values: Anti-inflammatory, boosts immunity.

Servings: 1

RECIPE N: 4 - Rosehip and Hibiscus Tea

Preparation Time: 10 minutes

Ingredients: Dried rosehip (1 tbsp), Dried hibiscus flowers (1 tbsp), Honey (optional, 1 tbsp), Boiling water (1 cup)

Method of Cooking: Steeping

Procedure: Steep dried rosehip and hibiscus flowers in boiling water for 5 minutes, strain, sweeten with honey if preferred.

Nutritional Values: High in vitamin C, antioxidants.

Servings: 1

Refreshing Non-Alcoholic Drinks

RECIPE N: 1 - Cucumber Mint Cooler

Preparation Time: 10 minutes
Ingredients: Cucumber (1, sliced), Fresh mint leaves (1/4 cup), Lime juice (2 tbsp), Sparkling water (2 cups), Honey (1 tbsp), Ice cubes
Method of Cooking: Mixing

Procedure: Muddle cucumber slices, mint leaves, lime juice, honey, top with sparkling water, serve over ice for a refreshing drink.
Nutritional Values: Hydrating, low in calories.
Servings: 2

RECIPE N: 2 - Pineapple Ginger Fizz

Preparation Time: 10 minutes

Ingredients: Pineapple juice (1 cup), Ginger ale (1 cup), Fresh ginger (1 tsp, grated), Lime juice (1 tbsp), Ice cubes, Pineapple slices (for garnish)
Method of Cooking: Mixing

Procedure: Mix pineapple juice, ginger ale, grated ginger, lime juice, serve over ice, garnish with pineapple slices for a tropical twist.
Nutritional Values: Rich in vitamin C and digestive aids.
Servings: 2

RECIPE N: 3 - Watermelon Basil Slush

Preparation Time: 15 minutes

Ingredients: Watermelon (2 cups, cubed and frozen), Basil leaves (1/4 cup), Lemon juice (2 tbsp), Honey (1 tbsp), Ice cubes
Method of Cooking: Blending

Procedure: Blend frozen watermelon, basil leaves, lemon juice, honey, ice until slushy consistency, serve immediately for a cooling refreshment.
Nutritional Values: High in antioxidants and hydration.
Servings: 2

RECIPE N: 4 - Berry Lemonade Spritzer

Preparation Time: 10 minutes

Ingredients: Mixed berries (1 cup), Lemon juice (1/4 cup), Honey (2 tbsp), Sparkling water (2 cups), Ice cubes, Lemon slices (for garnish)
Method of Cooking: Mixing

Procedure: Muddle mixed berries, mix with lemon juice, honey, add sparkling water, serve over ice, garnish with lemon slices.
Nutritional Values: Refreshing with a high vitamin content.
Servings: 2

Chapter 12: 45-Day Meal Plan

DAY	Breakfasts	Lunches	Snacks	Dinner
1	RECIPE N: 2 Berry Almond Bliss Bowl	RECIPE N° 1: Garden Fresh Quinoa Salad	RECIPE N: 1 - Apple Cinnamon Yogurt Bowl	RECIPE N: 1 - Grilled Chicken with Herb Quinoa
2	RECIPE N: 3 Green Power Smoothie Bowl	RECIPE N° 2: Crunchy Rainbow Slaw	RECIPE N: 2 - Veggie Sticks with Hummus	RECIPE N: 2 - Baked Salmon with Asparagus
3	ECIPE N: 4 Sunshine Citrus Bowl	RECIPE N° 3: Mediterranean Chickpea Salad	RECIPE N: 3 - Baked Kale Chips	RECIPE N: 3 - Turkey and Spinach Stuffed Bell Peppers
4	RECIPE N: 5 Red Velvet Beet Bowl	RECIPE N° 4: Avocado and Black Bean Salad	RECIPE N: 4 - Peanut Butter Banana Bites	RECIPE N: 4 - Lemon Garlic Shrimp Skewers
5	RECIPE N: 6 Peachy Green Bowl	RECIPE N° 5: Asian Sesame Tofu Salad	RECIPE N: 5 - Avocado Toast with Cherry Tomatoes	RECIPE N: 5 - Seared Tuna Steaks with Ginger Soy Glaze
6	RECIPE N: 7 Zesty Blueberry Bowl	RECIPE N° 6: Pear and Walnut Arugula Salad	RECIPE N: 6 - Spiced Roasted Chickpeas	RECIPE N: 6 - Herb-Crusted Cod with Zucchini Noodles
7	RECIPE N: 8 Tropical Avocado Bowl	RECIPE N° 7: Zesty Lentil and Beet Salad	RECIPE N: 7 - Greek Yogurt and	RECIPE N: 7 - Grilled Pork Tenderloin with Apple

			Mixed Berries	Salsa
8	RECIPE N: 9 Spiced Pear Oat Bowl	RECIPE N° 8: Spiced Chickpea and Quinoa Bowl	RECIPE N: 8 - Cucumber and Cream Cheese Bites	RECIPE N: 8 - Balsamic Glazed Chicken Breast
9	RECIPE N: 10 Antioxidant Acai Bowl	RECIPE N° 9: Summer Berry Spinach Salad	RECIPE N: 9 - Almond and Date Energy Balls	RECIPE N: 9 - Spiced Turkey Meatballs with Tomato Sauce
10	RECIPE N: 1 Mediterranean Veggie Scramble	RECIPE N° 10: Grilled Veggie and Hummus Wrap	RECIPE N: 10 - Caprese Skewers	RECIPE N: 10 - Garlic Lime Flank Steak
11	RECIPE N: 2 Herbed Mushroom Omelet	RECIPE N° 1: Velvet Butternut Squash Soup	RECIPE N: 1 - Roasted Red Pepper Hummus	RECIPE N: 1 - Stuffed Portobello Mushrooms
12	RECIPE N: 3 Spinach and Goat Cheese Scramble	RECIPE N° 2: Classic Lentil Soup	RECIPE N: 2 - Greek Tzatziki Dip	RECIPE N: 2 - Creamy Avocado Pasta
13	RECIPE N: 4 Tomato Basil Frittata	RECIPE N° 3: Tomato Basil Bisque	RECIPE N: 3 - Avocado and Cilantro Dip	RECIPE N: 3 - Eggplant Parmesan
14	RECIPE N: 5 Zucchini and Bell Pepper Mini Quiches	RECIPE N° 4: Garden Vegetable Broth	RECIPE N: 4 - Sun-Dried Tomato Pesto	RECIPE N: 4 - Vegetarian Chili
15	RECIPE N: 6 Asparagus and Parmesan Omelet	RECIPE N° 5: Spicy Black Bean Soup	RECIPE N: 5 - Classic Bean Dip	RECIPE N: 5 - Spinach and Ricotta Stuffed

			Shells
16	RECIPE N: 7 Smoked Salmon Scramble	RECIPE N: 6 - Spicy Black Bean Soup	RECIPE N: 6 - Spicy Mango Salsa	RECIPE N: 6 - Thai Tofu Stir-Fry
17	RECIPE N: 8 Sweet Potato and Kale Frittata	RECIPE N: 7 - Sweet Potato and Red Lentil Soup	RECIPE N: 7 - Creamy Spinach Artichoke Dip	RECIPE N: 7 - Caprese Stuffed Portobello Caps
18	RECIPE N: 9 Avocado and Egg White Wrap	RECIPE N: 8 - Classic Minestrone Soup	RECIPE N: 8 - Black Olive Tapenade	RECIPE N: 8 - Zucchini and Corn Quesadillas
19	RECIPE N: 10 Bell Pepper and Onion Frittata Muffins	RECIPE N: 9 - Roasted Red Pepper and Tomato Soup	RECIPE N: 9 - Roasted Garlic and White Bean Dip	RECIPE N: 9 - Creamy Mushroom Risotto
20	RECIPE N° 1: Sunrise Berry Smoothie Bowl	RECIPE N: 10 - Barley and Vegetable Soup	RECIPE N: 10 - Fiery Sichuan Eggplant Dip	RECIPE N: 10 - Baked Falafel with Tzatziki Sauce
21	RECIPE N° 2: Mediterranean Herb Omelet	RECIPE N: 1 - Avocado and Chickpea Hummus Wrap	RECIPE N: 1 - Almond Coconut Energy Bars	RECIPE N: 1 - Chicken and Broccoli Stir-Fry
22	RECIPE N° 3: Apple Cinnamon Quinoa Porridge	RECIPE N: 2 - Mediterranean Veggie Pita Pocket	RECIPE N: 2 - Peanut Butter Chocolate Chip Bites	RECIPE N: 2 - Shrimp and Asparagus Skillet
23	RECIPE N° 4: Tropical Bliss Smoothie Bowl	RECIPE N: 3 - Tofu Lettuce Wraps	RECIPE N: 3 - Cranberry Pistachio Energy	RECIPE N: 3 - Beef and Bell Pepper Stir-Fry

			Squares	
24	RECIPE N° 5: Spinach and Mushroom Scramble	RECIPE N: 4 - Grilled Vegetable and Hummus Sandwich	RECIPE N: 1 - Roasted Red Pepper Hummus	RECIPE N: 4 - Spicy Tofu and Vegetable Skillet
25	RECIPE N° 6: Peachy Keen Steel-Cut Oats	RECIPE N: 5 - Quinoa and Black Bean Burrito	RECIPE N: 1 - Apple Cinnamon Yogurt Bowl	RECIPE N: 5 - Lemon Garlic Chicken Skillet
26	RECIPE N° 7: Avocado and Tomato Scramble	RECIPE N: 9 - Roasted Red Pepper and Tomato Soup	RECIPE N: 2 - Veggie Sticks with Hummus	RECIPE N: 6 - Teriyaki Salmon Stir-Fry
27	RECIPE N° 8: Berry Almond Overnight Oats	RECIPE N: 1 - Avocado and Chickpea Hummus Wrap	RECIPE N: 3 - Baked Kale Chips	RECIPE N: 7 - Spicy Sausage and Kale Skillet
28	RECIPE N° 9: Green Goddess Smoothie Bowl	RECIPE N: 2 - Mediterranean Veggie Pita Pocket	RECIPE N: 4 - Peanut Butter Banana Bites	RECIPE N: 8 - Mushroom and Spinach Frittata
29	RECIPE N° 10: Savory Veggie Breakfast Bowl	RECIPE N: 3 - Tofu Lettuce Wraps	RECIPE N: 5 - Avocado Toast with Cherry Tomatoes	RECIPE N: 9 - Cauliflower and Chickpea Curry Skillet
30	RECIPE N: 1 ... Tropical Sunrise Smoothie Bowl	RECIPE N: 4 - Grilled Vegetable and Hummus Sandwich	RECIPE N: 6 - Spiced Roasted Chickpeas	RECIPE N: 10 - Skillet Lasagna
31	RECIPE N: 2 Berry Almond Bliss Bowl	RECIPE N: 5 - Quinoa and Black Bean Burrito	RECIPE N: 7 - Greek Yogurt	

			and Mixed Berries
32	RECIPE N: 3 Green Power Smoothie Bowl	RECIPE N: Smoked Salmon and Avocado Toast	RECIPE N: 8 - Cucumber and Cream Cheese Bites	RECIPE N: 1 - Grilled Chicken with Herb Quinoa
33	RECIPE N: 4 Sunshine Citrus Bowl	RECIPE N: Pesto Chicken Salad Wrap	RECIPE N: 9 - Almond and Date Energy Balls	RECIPE N: 2 - Baked Salmon with Asparagus
34	RECIPE N: 5 Red Velvet Beet Bowl	RECIPE N: Spicy Black Bean Burrito	RECIPE N: 10 - Caprese Skewers	RECIPE N: 3 - Turkey and Spinach Stuffed Bell Peppers
35	RECIPE N: 6 Peachy Green Bowl	RECIPE N: Curried Egg Salad Sandwich	RECIPE N: 1 - Roasted Red Pepper Hummus	RECIPE N: 4 - Lemon Garlic Shrimp Skewers
36	RECIPE N: 7 Zesty Blueberry Bowl	RECIPE N: Roast Beef and Horseradish Cream Cheese Roll-Up	RECIPE N: 2 - Greek Tzatziki Dip	RECIPE N: 5 - Seared Tuna Steaks with Ginger Soy Glaze
37	RECIPE N: 8 Tropical Avocado Bowl	RECIPE N: 1 - Avocado and Chickpea Hummus Wrap	RECIPE N: 3 - Avocado and Cilantro Dip	RECIPE N: 6 - Herb-Crusted Cod with Zucchini Noodles
38	RECIPE N: 9 Spiced Pear Oat Bowl	RECIPE N° 10: Grilled Veggie and Hummus Wrap	RECIPE N: 4 - Sun-Dried Tomato Pesto	RECIPE N: 7 - Grilled Pork Tenderloin with Apple Salsa

39	RECIPE N: 10 Antioxidant Acai Bowl	RECIPE N° 1: Velvet Butternut Squash Soup	RECIPE N: 5 - Classic Bean Dip	RECIPE N: 8 - Balsamic Glazed Chicken Breast
40	RECIPE N: 1 Mediterranean Veggie Scramble	RECIPE N° 2: Classic Lentil Soup	RECIPE N: 6 - Spicy Mango Salsa	RECIPE N: 9 - Spiced Turkey Meatballs with Tomato Sauce
41	RECIPE N: 2 Herbed Mushroom Omelet	RECIPE N° 3: Tomato Basil Bisque	RECIPE N: 7 - Creamy Spinach Artichoke Dip	RECIPE N: 10 - Garlic Lime Flank Steak
42	RECIPE N: 3 Spinach and Goat Cheese Scramble	RECIPE N° 4: Garden Vegetable Broth	RECIPE N: 8 - Black Olive Tapenade	RECIPE N: 1 - Stuffed Portobello Mushrooms
43	RECIPE N: 4 Tomato Basil Frittata	RECIPE N° 5: Spicy Black Bean Soup	RECIPE N: 9 - Roasted Garlic and White Bean Dip	RECIPE N: 2 - Creamy Avocado Pasta
44	RECIPE N: 5 Zucchini and Bell Pepper Mini Quiches	RECIPE N: 6 - Spicy Black Bean Soup	RECIPE N: 10 - Fiery Sichuan Eggplant Dip	RECIPE N: 3 - Eggplant Parmesan
45	RECIPE N: 2 Herbed Mushroom Omelet	RECIPE N° 3: Tomato Basil Bisque	RECIPE N: 7 - Creamy Spinach Artichoke Dip	RECIPE N: 10 - Garlic Lime Flank Steak

Weekly Shopping Lists

DAYS (1-7): Breakfast Ingredients:

- Mixed berries
- Almonds
- Yogurt
- Spinach
- Banana
- Citrus fruits (oranges, grapefruits)
- Beets

- Peaches
- Green leafy vegetables (kale, swiss chard)
- Blueberries
- Avocado
- Pineapple
- Mango

Lunch Ingredients:

- Quinoa
- Fresh garden vegetables (lettuce, tomatoes, cucumbers, carrots)
- Red cabbage
- Bell peppers
- Chickpeas

- Feta cheese
- Black beans
- Sesame seeds
- Tofu
- Asian dressing ingredients (soy sauce, rice vinegar, sesame oil)

- Pears
- Walnuts
- Arugula
- Lentils
- Beets

Snack Ingredients:

- Apples
- Cinnamon
- Vegetables for dipping (carrots, bell peppers, cucumber)

- Hummus
- Kale
- Peanut butter
- Cherry tomatoes
- Greek yogurt

- Mixed berries
- Chickpeas (for roasting)
- Spices (such as cumin, paprika)

Dinner Ingredients:

- Chicken breasts
- Herbs (such as parsley, thyme)
- Salmon fillets
- Asparagus
- Ground turkey

- Spinach
- Bell peppers
- Shrimp
- Garlic
- Tuna steaks
- Ginger

- Cod fillets
- Zucchini (for noodles)
- Pork tenderloin
- Apples

Breakfast Ingredients (Days 8-14):

- Pears
- Spices (cinnamon, nutmeg)
- Oats
- Acai berry puree or powder
- Various fresh berries (strawberries, blueberries)

- Mediterranean vegetables (tomatoes, onions, peppers)
- Eggs
- Hummus
- Mushrooms
- Butternut squash
- Spinach
- Goat cheese

- Basil
- Frittata ingredients (eggs, tomatoes, fresh basil)
- Zucchini
- Bell peppers
- Mini quiche ingredients (eggs, cream, cheese)

Lunch Ingredients (Days 8-14):

- Chickpeas
- Quinoa
- Spices (cumin, paprika, cayenne)
- Cream cheese
- Spinach leaves

- Summer berries
- Grilled vegetables (zucchini, eggplant, bell peppers)
- Butternut squash for soup

- Lentils
- Vegetable broth
- Garden vegetables for broth (carrots, celery, onion)

Snack Ingredients (Days 8-14):

- Cucumbers
- Dates
- Almonds
- Mozzarella cheese
- Tomatoes

- Basil leaves (for Caprese skewers)
- Greek yogurt (for Tzatziki)
- Avocado

- Cilantro
- Sun-dried tomatoes

- Pesto ingredients (basil, pine nuts or walnuts, garlic, Parmesan cheese)

Dinner Ingredients (Days 8-14):

- Chicken breasts
- Balsamic vinegar
- Ground turkey (for meatballs)
- Tomato sauce
- Flank steak
- spices)
- Lime
- Portobello mushrooms
- Red peppers (for roasting)
- Avocado (for creamy pasta)
- Pasta
- Eggplant
- Parmesan cheese
- Chili ingredients (beans, tomatoes, onions, garlic, chili

Breakfast

Ingredients (Days 15-21):

- Asparagus
- Parmesan cheese
- Eggs
- Smoked salmon
- Sweet potatoes
- Kale
- Avocado
- Egg whites
- Bell peppers
- Onions
- Various herbs (such as basil, parsley, dill for omelets and frittatas)

Snack Ingredients (Days 15-21):

- Classic bean dip ingredients (canned beans, seasonings)
- Mangoes (for salsa)
- Spinach
- Artichoke hearts (for dip)
- Black olives (for tapenade)
- Garlic
- White beans
- Almonds
- Coconut flakes (for energy bars)

Lunch Ingredients (Days 15-21):

- Black beans (for soup)
- Spices (cumin, chili powder for soup)
- Sweet potatoes (for soup)
  - vegetables (for vegetable soup)
- Red lentils
- Chickpeas (for hummus wrap)
- Whole grain wraps
  - Barley
- Various

Dinner Ingredients (Days 15-21):

- Spinach
- Ricotta cheese
- Jumbo pasta shells
- Tofu
- Thai stir-fry ingredients (soy sauce, vegetables, tofu)
- Portobello mushrooms
- Caprese ingredients (mozzarella, tomatoes, basil)
- Quesadilla ingredients (tortillas, cheese, zucchini, corn)
- Risotto rice (Arborio)
- Mushrooms (for risotto)
- Falafel ingredients (chickpeas, herbs, spices)
- Tzatziki sauce ingredients (Greek yogurt, cucumber, garlic)
- Chicken breasts
- Broccoli

Breakfast Ingredients (Days 22-28):

- Apples
- Cinnamon
- Quinoa
- Various tropical fruits (mango, pineapple, banana)
- Spinach
- Mushrooms
- Steel-cut oats
- Peaches
- Avocados
- Tomatoes
- Berries (strawberries, blueberries, raspberries)
- Almonds
- Green leafy vegetables (kale, spinach for the smoothie bowl)

Snack Ingredients (Days 22-28):

- Pita bread
- Peanut butter
- Chocolate chips
- Cranberries
- Pistachios
- Greek yogurt
- Kale
- Bananas

Lunch Ingredients (Days 22-28):

- Mediterranean veggies (cucumbers, olives, tomatoes)
- Tofu
- Lettuce leaves for wraps
- Hummus
- Quinoa
- Black beans
- Whole grain tortillas for burritos
- Roasted red peppers
- Chickpeas

Dinner Ingredients (Days 22-28):

- Shrimp
- Asparagus
- Beef (for stir-fry)
- Bell peppers
- Tofu (for spicy skillet)
- Chicken breasts
- Lemon
- Garlic
- Salmon (for teriyaki stir-fry)
- Sausage
- Kale
- Eggs (for frittata)
- Mushrooms
- Spinach

Breakfast Ingredients (Days 29-35):

- Various vegetables for a savory breakfast bowl (bell peppers, onions, spinach)
- leafy vegetables (kale, spinach)
- Fruits for smoothie bowls (mango, pineapple, berries)
- Almond milk
- Citrus fruits (oranges, grapefruits)
- Beets
- Peaches
- Green

Snack Ingredients (Days 29-35):

- Avocados
- Cherry tomatoes
- Bread (for toast)
- Chickpeas (for roasting)
- Greek yogurt
- Mixed berries
- Cream cheese
- Cucumbers
- Dates
- Almonds

Lunch Ingredients (Days 29-35):

- Tofu
- Lettuce (for wraps)
- Grilled vegetables (zucchini, bell peppers)
- Hummus
- Whole grain bread (for sandwiches)
- Quinoa
- Black beans (for burrito)
- Smoked salmon
- Chicken breast (for pesto wrap)
- Pesto sauce
- Egg salad ingredients (eggs, curry powder, mayonnaise)
- Black beans (for spicy burrito)

Dinner Ingredients (Days 29-35):

- Cauliflower
- Chickpeas (for curry)
- Curry spices
- Ground beef or turkey (for skillet lasagna)
- Lasagna noodles
- Tomato sauce
- Cheese
- Chicken breasts
- Herbs (for herb quinoa)
- Salmon fillets
- Asparagus
- Ground turkey (for stuffed bell peppers)
- Spinach
- Shrimp
- Garlic

Breakfast Ingredients (Days 36-45):

- Blueberries
- Oats
- Avocados
- Tropical fruits (pineapple, mango)
- Pears
- Spinach
- Goat cheese
- Eggs
- Tomatoes
- Basil
- Zucchini
- Bell peppers
- Mushrooms
- Various herbs (for seasoning omelets and frittatas)

Snack Ingredients (Days 36-45):

- Roast beef slices
- Horseradish
- Cream cheese
- Greek yogurt (for tzatziki)
- Cucumber
- Sun-dried tomatoes
- Pine nuts or walnuts (for pesto)
- Beans (for bean dip)
- Mango
- Chickpeas
- Artichoke hearts
- Black olives
- Garlic
- White beans
- Eggplant
- Sichuan sauce ingredients

Lunch Ingredients (Days 36-45):

- o Whole grain wraps
- o Hummus
- o Grilled vegetables (zucchini, eggplant, peppers)
- o vegetables)

- o Chickpeas
- o Butternut squash (for soup)
- o Lentils
- o Tomatoes (for bisque)

- o Vegetable broth ingredients (various garden

Dinner Ingredients (Days 36-45):

- o Tuna steaks
- o Ginger
- o Soy sauce
- o Cod fillets
- o Zucchini (for noodles)

- o Pork tenderloin
- o Apples (for salsa)
- o Chicken breasts
- o Balsamic vinegar
- o Turkey (for meatballs)

- o Tomato sauce
- o Flank steak
- o Portobello mushrooms
- o Avocado (for pasta)
- o Eggplant (for parmesan

Daily Meal Schedules

Tips for Preparing and Storing Meals

In the journey toward holistic wellness, especially for women who have experienced gallbladder removal and are devoted to maintaining an active yoga practice, the art of meal preparation and preservation is a cornerstone. This chapter is not just about prepping meals; it's about embracing a lifestyle that nourishes both the body and the spirit.

Embracing Mindful Meal Preparation

The process of preparing your meals should be as nourishing for your spirit as the food is for your body. This mindfulness in the kitchen creates a harmonious environment that infuses your meals with positive energy.

Creating a Sacred Space: Your kitchen is more than a room; it's a sanctuary where nourishment begins. Keep it organized and infuse it with elements that bring joy – be it fresh flowers, soothing music, or aromatic candles.

Intentional Cooking: As you cook, focus on the intention behind each meal. Whether it's to heal, energize, or provide comfort, this intentionality adds a deeper dimension to your cooking.

Love and Gratitude: Infuse your food with love and gratitude. A meal prepared with a grateful heart carries that energy and enhances the overall dining experience.

Efficient and Effective Meal Prep

Meal prepping is a practical approach that saves time and ensures you have healthy, gallbladder-friendly meals ready throughout the week.

Plan Your Meals: Take some time each week to plan your meals. This planning should align with the weekly shopping lists and daily meal schedules outlined in the previous chapters.

Batch Cooking: Cook in batches. This not only saves time but also ensures consistency in your diet. Soups, stews, and casseroles are excellent options for batch cooking.

Versatile Ingredients: Focus on ingredients that can be used in multiple ways. Quinoa, for instance, can be a breakfast porridge, a salad base, or a side for dinner.

Prep Components Separately: Prepare components like grains, proteins, and veggies separately and mix and match them for variety throughout the week.

Smart Storage Solutions

Proper storage is crucial in maintaining the freshness and nutritional value of your meals.

Invest in Quality Containers: Use high-quality, airtight containers to keep your food fresh. Glass containers are preferable as they are environmentally friendly and don't harbor bacteria like plastic can.

Label and Date: Always label and date your containers. This practice helps in keeping track of freshness and ensures food safety.

Freeze for Longevity: Some meals or components like soups and cooked grains can be frozen to extend their shelf life. Freezing in appropriate portion sizes makes it easy to defrost only what you need.

Staying Inspired and Creative

Keep your meal prep exciting by trying new recipes or experimenting with different herbs and spices. This continuous culinary exploration keeps your diet interesting and engaging.

Seasonal Varieties: Embrace the seasons in your cooking. Use seasonal produce for freshness and to add variety to your diet throughout the year.

Themed Meal Days: Introduce themed meal days, like "Meatless Monday" or "Soup Saturday", to add an element of fun to your meal planning.

Involve Family or Friends: Occasionally, involve your family or friends in meal prepping. This not only makes the process enjoyable but also helps in sharing your journey towards holistic wellness.

Educational Aspect

As a yoga practitioner and educator, sharing these meal prep and preservation tips with your students can be empowering. It allows them to see the connection between what we eat, how we prepare it, and our overall well-being. This holistic approach to food can be a powerful tool in their wellness journey.

Workshops and Classes: Consider hosting workshops or classes focused on healthy meal prep and storage techniques. This can be an extension of your yoga teaching, offering a more comprehensive approach to wellness.

Tips for Meal Prepping and Storage

In the journey toward holistic wellness, especially for women who have experienced gallbladder removal and are devoted to maintaining an active yoga practice, the art of meal preparation and preservation is a cornerstone. This chapter is not just about prepping meals; it's about embracing a lifestyle that nourishes both the body and the spirit.

Embracing Mindful Meal Preparation

The process of preparing your meals should be as nourishing for your spirit as the food is for your body. This mindfulness in the kitchen creates a harmonious environment that infuses your meals with positive energy.

Creating a Sacred Space: Your kitchen is more than a room; it's a sanctuary where nourishment begins. Keep it organized and infuse it with elements that bring joy – be it fresh flowers, soothing music, or aromatic candles.

Intentional Cooking: As you cook, focus on the intention behind each meal. Whether it's to heal, energize, or provide comfort, this intentionality adds a deeper dimension to your cooking.

Love and Gratitude: Infuse your food with love and gratitude. A meal prepared with a grateful heart carries that energy and enhances the overall dining experience.

Efficient and Effective Meal Prep

Meal prepping is a practical approach that saves time and ensures you have healthy, gallbladder-friendly meals ready throughout the week.

Plan Your Meals: Take some time each week to plan your meals. This planning should align with the weekly shopping lists and daily meal schedules outlined in the previous chapters.

Batch Cooking: Cook in batches. This not only saves time but also ensures consistency in your diet. Soups, stews, and casseroles are excellent options for batch cooking.

Versatile Ingredients: Focus on ingredients that can be used in multiple ways. Quinoa, for instance, can be a breakfast porridge, a salad base, or a side for dinner.

Prep Components Separately: Prepare components like grains, proteins, and veggies separately and mix and match them for variety throughout the week.

Smart Storage Solutions

Proper storage is crucial in maintaining the freshness and nutritional value of your meals.

Invest in Quality Containers: Use high-quality, airtight containers to keep your food fresh. Glass containers are preferable as they are environmentally friendly and don't harbor bacteria like plastic can.

Label and Date: Always label and date your containers. This practice helps in keeping track of freshness and ensures food safety.

Freeze for Longevity: Some meals or components like soups and cooked grains can be frozen to extend their shelf life. Freezing in appropriate portion sizes makes it easy to defrost only what you need.

Staying Inspired and Creative

Keep your meal prep exciting by trying new recipes or experimenting with different herbs and spices. This continuous culinary exploration keeps your diet interesting and engaging.

Seasonal Varieties: Embrace the seasons in your cooking. Use seasonal produce for freshness and to add variety to your diet throughout the year.

Themed Meal Days: Introduces themed meal days, like "Meatless Monday" or "Soup Saturday", to add an element of fun to your meal planning.

Involve Family or Friends: Occasionally, involve your family or friends in meal prepping. This not only makes the process enjoyable but also helps in sharing your journey towards holistic wellness.

Educational Aspect

As a yoga practitioner and educator, sharing these meal prep and preservation tips with your students can be empowering. It allows them to see the connection between what we eat, how we prepare it, and our overall well-being. This holistic approach to food can be a powerful tool in their wellness journey.

Workshops and Classes: Consider hosting workshops or classes focused on healthy meal prep and storage techniques. This can be an extension of your yoga teaching, offering a more comprehensive approach to wellness.

Measurement Conversion Table

Volume Equivalents (Liquid)

US Standard	US Standard (ounces)	Metric (approximate)
2 tablespoons	1 fl. oz.	30 mL
¼ cup	2 fl. oz.	60 mL
half cup	4 fl. oz.	120 mL
1 cup	8 fl. oz.	240 mL
1 half cups	12 fl. oz.	355 mL
2 cups or 1 pint	16 fl. oz.	457 mL
4 cups or 1 quart	32 fl. oz.	1 L
1 gallon	128 fl. oz.	4 L

Volume Equivalents (Dry)

US Standard	Metric (approximate)
1/8 teaspoon	0.5 mL
¼ teaspoon	1 mL
half teaspoon	2 mL
¾ teaspoon	4 mL
1 teaspoon	5 mL
1 tablespoon	15 mL
¼ cup	59 mL
1/3 cup	79 mL
half cup	118 mL
2/3 cup	156 mL
¾ cup	177 mL
1 cup	235 mL
2 cups or 1 pint	475 mL
3 cups	700 mL
4 cups or 1 quart	1 L

Oven Temperatures

Fahrenheit (F)	Celsius (C) (approximate)
250°F	120°C
300°F	150°C
325°F	165°C
350°F	180°C
375°F	190°C
400°F	200°C
425°F	220°C
450°F	230°C

Weight Equivalents

US Standard	Metric (approximate)
1 tablespoon	15 g
half ounce	15 g
1 ounce	30 g
2 ounces	60 g
4 ounces	115 g
8 ounces	225 g
12 ounces	340 g
16 ounces or 1 pound or 1 lb	455 g

Chapter 13: Conclusion: Your Journey Ahead

Staying Motivated and Committed

The journey to wellness, especially after a significant change like gallbladder removal, is akin to navigating a river with its ebbs and flows. Staying motivated and committed is not just about adhering to a diet or routine; it's about embracing a lifestyle that resonates with your innermost self, especially for women who have integrated the practice of yoga into their lives. This chapter is dedicated to nurturing that flame of motivation and commitment, ensuring it burns bright as you continue on your path to holistic wellness.

Understanding the Depths of Motivation

Motivation is a deeply personal and dynamic force. It's what gets you started and keeps you on the path to achieving your goals. Understanding what motivates you is the key to maintaining it. Is it the desire to continue your active yoga practice without dietary interruptions? Or perhaps it's the aspiration to educate others about holistic wellness. Identifying these driving forces is the first step in staying motivated.

Creating a Vision

Begin by visualizing your goals. Visualization is a powerful tool used in both yoga and wellness. Imagine yourself leading a yoga class, feeling strong, energetic, and healthy. Visualize the foods that nourish and revitalize your body. This mental imagery serves as a constant reminder of what you're striving towards.

Setting Realistic and Achievable Goals

It's important to set goals that are realistic and achievable. Breaking down your larger vision into smaller, manageable goals makes the journey less overwhelming and more attainable. For instance, instead of a vague goal like "eat healthier," set a specific goal such as "incorporate two servings of vegetables into every meal."

Celebrating Milestones

Every step forward is a victory and deserves recognition. Celebrate your milestones, no matter how small they may seem. Whether it's mastering a new yoga pose, trying a new recipe, or just feeling more energetic, acknowledging these achievements fuels further motivation.

Building a Supportive Community

Surround yourself with people who support and share your journey. Join or create a community of individuals who have undergone gallbladder removal and are passionate about yoga and wellness. Share experiences, recipes, and tips. This sense of community fosters accountability and encouragement.

Embracing Flexibility

Flexibility in approach is crucial. Understand that there will be days when things don't go as planned. Instead of being hard on yourself, embrace these moments as part of the journey. Adapt and learn from them.

Incorporating Mindfulness

Mindfulness is a core component of both yoga and holistic wellness. Practice being present in every action, be it while eating, exercising, or even resting. This mindfulness enhances the connection with your body and its needs, helping you stay committed to your wellness journey.

Finding Inspiration

Seek out sources of inspiration. It could be a book, a podcast, a person, or even nature. Inspiration can reignite your passion and motivation, especially during challenging times.

Documenting Your Journey

Keep a journal of your journey. Documenting your experiences, thoughts, and feelings is not only therapeutic but also serves as a tangible record of your progress. Looking back at how far you've come can be incredibly motivating.

Staying Educated

Continuously educate yourself about health, nutrition, and wellness. Knowledge is empowering and fuels motivation. Attend workshops, read the latest research, and stay informed about new practices in yoga and diet.

Integrating Yoga and Diet

Remember, your diet and yoga practice are deeply interconnected. A nutritious diet enhances your yoga practice, and yoga, in turn, fosters a deeper understanding of your body's nutritional needs. This symbiotic relationship is central to maintaining your motivation and commitment.

Staying motivated and committed on your journey post-gallbladder removal is an evolving process that requires patience, understanding, and self-compassion. It's about finding joy in the small steps, learning from the challenges, and embracing the journey as a whole. With each passing day, you're not only moving closer to your goals but also deepening your understanding of holistic wellness, which you can then share with others, especially your yoga students. This journey is not just about personal growth; it's about becoming a beacon of inspiration and knowledge for those around you.

Adapting and Personalizing Your Diet

Embarking on a post-gallbladder removal journey intertwines with the quest for a diet that is not only nourishing but also aligns with your unique bodily needs, especially for those who are devoted to an active yoga practice. This section delves into the art of personalizing your diet, a process that blends intuition with understanding, ensuring that what you eat resonates with both your physical and spiritual well-being.

Understanding Your Body's Language

First and foremost, listen to your body. It communicates in subtle cues and reactions, especially when it comes to food. After gallbladder removal, your digestive system undergoes a transformation, and it's crucial to recognize how different foods affect you. For instance, you might find that certain foods you once loved no longer agree with you, while others you hadn't considered become new staples.

The Role of Experimentation

Adapting your diet is a journey of experimentation. Start by introducing new foods slowly and in small quantities. Pay close attention to how you feel after eating them. Do they give you energy, or do they make you feel sluggish? Do they support your yoga practice, or do they cause discomfort? This mindful approach to eating allows you to build a diet that's tailored to your unique needs.

Creating a Flexible Diet Plan

Flexibility is key. Your body's needs will change based on a myriad of factors like stress levels, physical activity, and even the changing seasons. A diet plan that's too rigid doesn't accommodate these fluctuations. Instead, aim for a flexible plan that allows you to adjust based on your current needs.

Incorporating a Variety of Nutrients

Ensure your diet is well-rounded and inclusive of all the necessary nutrients. This means a healthy balance of carbohydrates, proteins, and fats, alongside vitamins and minerals. For instance, while focusing on lean proteins, don't forget the importance of fiber-rich vegetables and whole grains, as well as healthy fats like avocados and nuts.

Balancing Traditional Knowledge with Modern Science

Combine the wisdom of traditional eating practices with the knowledge offered by modern nutrition science. For instance, Ayurveda and traditional Chinese medicine offer insights into how different foods affect your body's energy and balance. Modern nutrition science, on the other hand, provides a detailed understanding of macros and micros, helping you build a nutritionally complete diet.

Personalizing Your Diet to Support Yoga Practice

As someone committed to yoga, it's vital to tailor your diet to support your practice. This could mean a lighter meal before a yoga session to avoid discomfort or a protein-rich meal afterward to aid in muscle recovery. Listen to your body and adjust your diet based on the intensity and style of your yoga practice.

Learning from Others, Yet Staying True to Yourself

While it's beneficial to seek advice from nutritionists, dieticians, or fellow yoga practitioners, remember that what works for one person may not work for you. Use their advice as a guideline, but always bring it back to how it aligns with your body and your needs.

The Role of Mindfulness in Eating

Bring mindfulness into your eating habits. This means eating slowly, savoring each bite, and being present during meals. This practice not only enhances your relationship with food but also improves digestion and satisfaction with meals.

Documenting Your Dietary Journey

Consider keeping a food journal. Document what you eat, how you feel afterward, and any reactions you notice. Over time, patterns will emerge, guiding you towards the best dietary choices for your body.

Embracing Change with Grace

Finally, embrace the ever-evolving nature of your dietary needs with grace and openness. What works today might not work tomorrow, and that's okay. It's all part of the journey towards finding the perfect balance for your body and lifestyle.

Adapting and personalizing your diet post-gallbladder removal is an intimate and evolving journey. It's about creating harmony between your body's needs and your food choices, ensuring that each meal supports not just your physical health but also your spiritual well-being as a yoga practitioner. By listening to your body, being flexible, and embracing the journey with an open heart, you cultivate a relationship with food that is both nourishing and fulfilling. This personalized approach to nutrition becomes a cornerstone of your overall health and wellness journey, empowering you to live your life to the fullest.

Continuing Your Health and Wellness Journey

The journey to health and wellness, especially after undergoing gallbladder removal, is a profound transformation that extends beyond dietary changes. It is a comprehensive evolution that encompasses your physical, mental, and spiritual well-being. This journey, particularly for women deeply involved in yoga and holistic wellness, is a continuous path of learning, growth, and self-discovery.

Embracing Holistic Health as a Way of Life

Holistic health is a multi-faceted approach that involves nurturing all aspects of your being. It's about looking beyond the food on your plate and considering other factors that contribute to your well-being.

- **Mindful Movement:** Yoga is an excellent practice that aligns with holistic health. It's not just a form of exercise; it's a way to connect with your body, breath, and mind. Regular yoga practice enhances flexibility, strength, and mental clarity.

- **Mental Well-being:** Paying attention to your mental health is as crucial as taking care of your physical body. Techniques such as meditation, deep breathing, and mindfulness can help manage stress, improve mental focus, and foster a sense of peace.

- **Emotional Balance:** Acknowledge and honor your emotions. Practices like journaling, engaging in creative activities, or talking with a therapist can be effective in processing emotions healthily.

Nourishing Relationships and Community

Human connection plays a vital role in your wellness journey. Building a supportive community can provide encouragement, share knowledge, and create a sense of belonging.

- **Community Involvement:** Join or create support groups for those who have undergone gallbladder removal. Sharing experiences and tips can be incredibly empowering.

- **Teaching and Sharing:** As a yoga practitioner, you have the unique opportunity to share your knowledge and experiences with others. Teaching yoga or conducting workshops on holistic well-being can be fulfilling ways to give back to your community.

Lifelong Learning and Growth

The field of health and wellness is ever-evolving. Staying informed and open to new information is key to your growth on this journey.

- **Continuous Education:** Attend seminars, read books, and stay updated with the latest research in nutrition and wellness. This knowledge not only benefits you but also those you teach.

- **Experimentation and Adaptation:** Be open to trying new wellness practices. What works for you now might change, and it's important to adapt and find what resonates with you at different stages of your life.

Sustainable Practices and Environmental Awareness

Your wellness journey is also about being mindful of the environment. Sustainable practices in your daily life can positively impact your health and the planet.

- **Eco-friendly Choices:** From the food you eat to the products you use, making eco-friendly choices can enhance your health. For example, choosing organic, locally-grown produce reduces your exposure to harmful chemicals and supports local farmers.

- **Reducing Carbon Footprint:** Simple actions like reducing plastic use, recycling, and conserving water contribute to a healthier environment.

Personal Reflection and Self-Care

Self-care is an integral part of your wellness journey. It's about taking time for yourself and honoring your body's needs.

- **Regular Self-Reflection:** Take time to reflect on your progress, acknowledge your achievements, and set goals for the future.

- **Holistic Self-Care Practices:** Incorporate self-care rituals that nourish you physically, mentally, and emotionally. This could include spa days, nature walks, or engaging in hobbies that bring you joy.

Your health and wellness journey post-gallbladder removal are a lifelong path filled with discoveries, challenges, and triumphs. It's a journey that goes beyond just managing a condition; it's about embracing a lifestyle that fosters complete well-being. By staying committed to holistic practices, nurturing your relationships, continuously learning, practicing sustainability, and prioritizing self-care, you create a life that is not just about surviving but thriving. This journey empowers you to live your fullest life, inspiring those around you, especially your yoga students, to embark on their paths to holistic wellness.

Made in United States
North Haven, CT
07 July 2024

54483748R00063